Nelson Advanced Modular Science

Systems and their Maintenance

JOHN ADDS • ERICA LARKCOM • RUTH MILLER

Nelson

Thomas Nelson and Sons Ltd
Nelson House
Mayfield Road
Walton-on-Thames
Surrey
KT12 5PL
United Kingdom

© John Adds, Erica Larkcom, Ruth Miller 1998

I(T)P Thomas Nelson is an International Thomson Publishing Company
I(T)P is used under licence

First published by Thomas Nelson and Sons Ltd 1998

ISBN 0-17-448268-X
NPN 9 8 7 6 5 4 3 2

Typesetting and artwork: Hardlines, Charlbury, Oxfordshire

Printed in China

Picture Research by Image Select International Ltd

Acquisitions: Mary Ashby/Chris Coyer
Editorial Management: Simon Bell
Editorial: Liz Jones
Production: Liam Reardon
Marketing: Jane Lewis
Design: Maria Pritchard

Acknowledgements

The authors wish to thank David Hartley for his help and encouragement during the preparation of the text.

Ruth Miller: figure 1.5(b), page 6; figure 6.12, page 123; CNRI/Science Photo Library: figure 1.7(a), page 8; Dr Tony Brain/Science Photo Library: figure 1.7(b), page 8; Manfred Kage/Science Photo Library: figure 1.13, page 14; John Adds: figure 1.16 (upper), page 16; figure 1.17, page 17; figure 2.17, page 38; figure 4.6, page 79; figure 5.1 (b), page 87; Professor P. M. Motta & M. Castellucci/Science Photo Library: figure 1.16 (lower), page 16; Dr Jeremy Burgess/Science Photo Library: figure 2.6 (upper left), page 28; Science Photo Library: figure 2.14, page 36; Anne Stephens: figure 3.1(b); Erica Clark: figure 3.1 (a), figure 3.2 (both),

page 58; figure 3.4, page 59; figure 3.6 (both), page 62; Sinclair Stammers/Science Photo Library: figure 3.3, page 59; Geoscience Features: figure 3.7, page 63; Dr P. Marazzi/ Science Photo Library: figure 5.26, page 109; Andrew Syred/Science Photo Library: figure 6.1, page 111; figure 6.9 (top), page 120; Oxford Scientific Films/ G. I. Bernard: figure 6.4, page 113; David Scharf/Science Photo Library: figure 6.9 (bottom), page 120; John McFarland/Science Photo Library: figure 6.28, page 145; James Holmes/Cellmark Diagnostics/Science Photo Library: figure 6.31, page 150

The examination questions and mark schemes on pages 153 to 166 are reproduced by permission of London Examinations, a division of Edexcel Foundation

Contents

Introduction

As modularisation of syllabuses gains momentum, there is a corresponding demand for a modular format in supporting texts. The Nelson Advanced Modular Science series has been written by Chief Examiners and those involved directly with the A level examinations. The books are based on the London Examinations (Edexcel) AS and A level modular syllabuses in Biology and Human Biology, Chemistry and Physics. Each module text offers complete and self-contained coverage of all the topics in the module. The texts also include examples outside the prescribed syllabus to broaden your understanding and help to illustrate the principle which is being presented. There are practical investigations and regular review questions to stimulate your thinking while you read about and study the topic. Finally, there are typical examination questions with mark schemes so that you can test yourself and help you to understand how to approach the examination.

Systems and their Maintenance is the third book in the Biology series. Here the text explores inside living organisms – to find out about the systems which allow living processes to occur and which contribute to the functioning of the whole organism. We look first at exchanges between organisms and the surrounding environment and then at the way materials are transported around, inside the plant or animal. For a multicellular organism to function as a whole, there must be coordination within the organism and responses to external stimuli from the environment. You will be able to compare the role of chemical coordination in plants and in animals, see the importance of nervous control in mammals and gain an understanding of homeostatic mechanisms. The strategies for reproduction as a means of perpetuating the species are reviewed in both plants and animals. Where possible, the biology is set in the context of its relevance to everyday life – with, for example, an insight into how plant growth substances can be used to manipulate crop growth, an appreciation of the events which show up in an electrocardiogram (ECG), or a consideration of modern reproductive technologies and their future applications in human populations. The authors hope that through your study of biology and with an understanding of the physiology of systems in living organisms, you will see how their internal environment is maintained and how they respond to changes in the external environment and ensure the long term survival of the species.

Erica Larkcom B.A., M.A., C.Biol., Subject Officer for A level Biology, formerly Head of Biology, Great Cornard Upper School, Suffolk

John Adds B.A., C.Biol., M.I.Biol., Chief Examiner for A level Biology, Head of Biology, Abbey Tutorial College, London

Ruth Miller B.Sc., C.Biol., M.I.Biol., Chief Examiner for AS and A level Biology, formerly Head of Biology, Sir William Perkins's School, Chertsey

Exchanges with the environment

Exchange processes

All living organisms constantly need to exchange materials with the environment in order to survive and grow. All organisms need to respire to release energy from their food. Most take up oxygen from the environment and, as a consequence of the catabolic reactions involved, release carbon dioxide as a waste product. **Heterotrophic** organisms require a ready-made source of food, which they obtain from their environment. This food consists of complex organic compounds, which need to be digested into simple, soluble molecules. Any undigested material is egested and thus returned to the environment.

Autotrophic organisms make their own organic nutrients from simple, inorganic molecules. In order to achieve this, they need to obtain the raw materials from their environment. Green plants are photoautotrophs, so use light energy in the process of photosynthesis. Carbon dioxide from the atmosphere, together with water and mineral ions from the soil, are used in the synthesis of all the organic molecules needed for growth and reproduction. In this process, the waste product is oxygen, which is returned to the atmosphere.

All organisms produce waste products as a result of their metabolic processes. In autotrophic organisms, the main excretory products are carbon dioxide from respiration and oxygen from photosynthesis. Any other waste substances are usually converted to insoluble, harmless compounds, which are stored in places such as the heartwood and bark of trees. The rate of metabolism of autotrophic organisms is much slower, so these waste substances are not produced in large quantities.

In heterotrophic organisms, where the rate of metabolism is faster, carbon dioxide is also produced, together with nitrogenous waste substances, which can become toxic if allowed to accumulate. These nitrogenous substances, together with any other compounds in excess of requirements, are excreted.

The physical processes involved with such exchanges are:
- **passive** – such as diffusion involved in the exchange of gases in the leaves of flowering plants
- **active** – as in the uptake of mineral ions against concentration gradients in the roots of flowering plants and the ventilation movements involved with respiratory mechanisms in insects and mammals.

The nature of exchange surfaces

Exchange surfaces are the sites where materials are exchanged between the organism and the environment. In simple organisms, this process occurs over the entire surface but in more complex, multicellular organisms there are specialised regions adapted for a particular function. Most of the exchanges

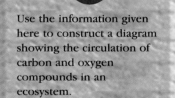

Use the information given here to construct a diagram showing the circulation of carbon and oxygen compounds in an ecosystem.

EXCHANGES WITH THE ENVIRONMENT

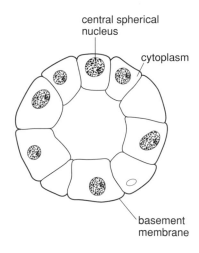

Figure 1.1 Cuboidal epithelium

between flowering plants and their environment occur through the roots or through the aerial parts, particularly the leaves. In mammals, most exchanges occur internally and involve epithelial tissues.

Epithelial tissues are found on the internal and external surfaces of organs and may have several roles depending on their location. Many epithelia protect underlying tissues against water loss, abrasion, pressure or infection. In addition, epithelial tissues may be involved in processes such as respiratory gas exchange, the uptake or release of nutrients and excretion.

A **simple epithelium** consists of cells arranged in a single layer, whereas **compound** or **stratified epithelia** are composed of several layers of cells. The compound epithelia, being thicker, often form impervious barriers on the external surface, but the simple epithelia form efficient exchange surfaces.

The main features of simple epithelial tissues are that:
* they form continuous layers on internal and external surfaces
* the cells are held together by a thin layer of intercellular substance containing hyaluronic acid
* the cells rest on a basement membrane made up largely of collagen fibres
* there are no blood cells present
* the free surfaces of the cells may be highly specialised
* damaged cells are rapidly replaced by cell division.

Cuboidal epithelium is the simplest type of epithelium and consists of cube-shaped cells, each with a centrally-situated spherical nucleus. The cells are closely packed together and appear pentagonal or hexagonal in outline when viewed from above. This type of epithelium occurs in the nephrons of the kidney and lines the salivary and pancreatic ducts. It is also present in many glands (mucus, salivary, sweat and thyroid) where it has a secretory function.

Squamous epithelium consists of thin, flattened cells with little cytoplasm. The nucleus of each cell is disc-shaped and centrally situated. Cytoplasmic connections exist between adjacent cells. The cells fit closely together and, when viewed from above, the margins of the cells are seen to be irregular (tesselated). This type of epithelium is found in the Bowman's capsule of the

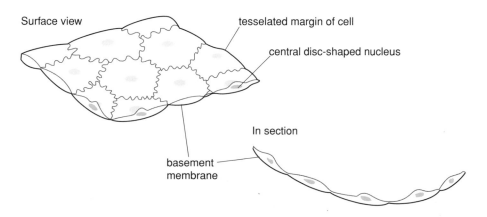

Figure 1.2 Squamous epithelium

kidney, the alveoli of the lungs and lining the blood vessels and the chambers of the heart.

Columnar epithelium is made up of tall, narrow cells. A large spherical nucleus is situated near the base of each cell and the free surface often possesses **microvilli**. Mucus-secreting goblet cells are often found amongst the columnar cells. This tissue lines the stomach and intestine, and is also present in some ducts of the kidney and in the thyroid gland.

Respiratory gas exchange

As has already been mentioned, aerobic respiration is common to most living organisms and necessitates the uptake of oxygen and the release of carbon dioxide. Respiring cells are constantly using up oxygen and releasing carbon dioxide, so concentration gradients exist between the organism and its environment with respect to these gases. Usually, within the organism there will be a lower concentration of oxygen and a higher concentration of carbon dioxide than in the environment, so oxygen tends to diffuse in and carbon dioxide diffuses out.

It must be remembered that the situation is slightly different in green plants. Respiration takes place all the time, so oxygen is continually taken up by respiring cells and carbon dioxide is released. During the hours of daylight, photosynthesis will occur in the palisade and spongy cells in the mesophyll of the leaves, involving the uptake of carbon dioxide and the release of oxygen. As this process takes place at a more rapid rate than respiration, during the day the concentration gradients of oxygen and carbon dioxide are reversed: carbon dioxide diffuses in and oxygen diffuses out.

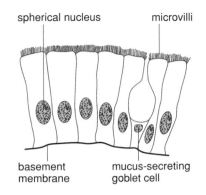

spherical nucleus   microvilli

basement membrane   mucus-secreting goblet cell

Figure 1.3 Columnar epithelium

Table 1.1 *Gas exchange in flowering plants*

Feature	Day	Night
respiration occurring	✓	✓
photosynthesis occurring	✓	✗
state of stomata	open	closed
concentration of CO_2 in leaf	low	high
concentration of CO_2 in atmosphere	higher	lower
concentration of O_2 in leaf	high	low
concentration of O_2 in atmosphere	lower	higher
net gas exchange	O_2 diffuses out CO_2 diffuses in	CO_2 diffuses out O_2 diffuses in

The site of respiratory gas exchange is referred to as the respiratory surface and, in order for gas exchange to be efficient, it has special features.

Features of gas exchange surfaces

The features of gas exchange surfaces, or respiratory surfaces, are determined by the factors which affect the rate of diffusion. We have already seen that the rate of diffusion will depend on the existence of concentration gradients, but

other factors that need to be considered are:
- the area over which diffusion occurs
- the distance over which diffusion occurs
- the nature of any barrier through which the molecules must pass
- the nature of the diffusing molecules.

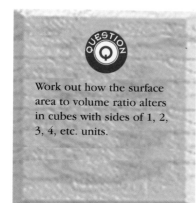

Work out how the surface area to volume ratio alters in cubes with sides of 1, 2, 3, 4, etc. units.

The area of the respiratory surface must be large enough to provide sufficient oxygen for the organism's requirements. In very small organisms, such as the unicellular *Amoeba*, where the surface area : volume ratio is large, the general body surface is the respiratory surface. In such organisms, gas exchange takes place through the cell surface membrane, oxygen diffusing in and carbon dioxide diffusing out. With larger, multicellular organisms, an increase in volume results in a decrease in the surface area : volume ratio, in other words there is less surface area per unit volume of organism and exchange of gases through the body surface may not be enough to satisfy the organism's needs. In such cases, specialised respiratory surfaces exist in the form of lungs or gills, providing a large area over which the exchange can occur.

In small organisms, the distances over which the diffusion of the gases occurs are small, but with increase in size there is a corresponding increase in bulk. This results in an increase in the distance of the respiring cells from the respiratory surface, slowing the rate of diffusion. In some larger organisms such as the flatworms, where there is no special respiratory surface, the body is flattened. This increases the efficiency of diffusion as no respiring cells are far from the respiratory surface. In other organisms where specialised respiratory surfaces are present, other mechanisms have evolved which improve the efficiency of gas exchange. A ventilation mechanism often exists, bringing fresh supplies of air or water in contact with the respiratory surface and maintaining a high concentration of oxygen. In addition, the concentration gradients are maintained by an internal transport system, such as the blood circulatory system, which brings deoxygenated blood to the respiratory surface and removes the oxygenated blood. In such cases, the oxygen-carrying capacity of the blood is increased by the presence of a respiratory pigment. In mammals, this pigment is **haemoglobin** and is present in specialised blood cells, erythrocytes.

The respiratory surface needs to be permeable to the respiratory gases. All cell surface membranes are permeable to oxygen, carbon dioxide and water.

Gas exchange in flowering plants

As has been discussed earlier, flowering plants carry out both respiration and photosynthesis, so the net gas exchange varies according to the time of day. During photosynthesis, molecules of ATP (adenosine triphosphate) are built up from ADP (adenosine diphosphate) and inorganic phosphate. This ATP is available to drive metabolic reactions, so we might ask ourselves, why do plants need to respire? If we think about this, we realise that photosynthesis only takes place in the light and only in those parts of the plant that have cells containing chloroplasts. Energy is needed in other, non-green regions of the plant, especially the roots. This energy is supplied through respiration of the carbon compounds synthesised in the leaves. In addition, the reactions of glycolysis and Krebs, cycle provide important intermediates in the synthesis of organic compounds required by the plant.

Gas exchange in flowering plants involves the aerial parts, mainly the leaves and stems. Leaves have a large surface area: volume ratio, which is favourable for the exchange of gases. Access to the respiring cells is by means of **stomata**, which are pores in the epidermis of the leaves. Inside the leaf, the large intercellular air spaces in the spongy mesophyll facilitate the diffusion of gases and the cells bordering these air spaces increase the total area available for gas exchange still further. During the day, when photosynthesis is occurring, the fixation of carbon dioxide maintains a concentration gradient of carbon dioxide between the interior of the leaf and the external atmosphere. The rate of diffusion of carbon dioxide is directly proportional to the concentration gradient, but it is also affected by factors such as the number and size of the stomata, the cuticle of the leaf and the layer of air surrounding the leaf. As these are all factors which also affect the movement of water in the plant, they will be described in more detail in Chapter 2.

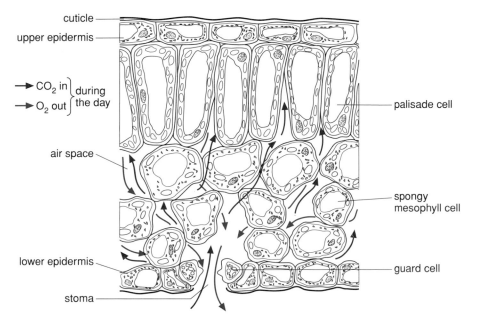

cuticle

upper epidermis

CO_2 in during

O_2 out the day

palisade cell

air space

spongy mesophyll cell

lower epidermis

guard cell

stoma

Figure 1.4 Vertical section through leaf lamina to show gas exchange surfaces and gas exchange during the day

In addition to the stomata on the leaves, gas exchange in woody plants takes place through structures called **lenticels**. As a result of the growth of the secondary xylem in a woody stem, the epidermis ruptures and is replaced by a layer of cork (phellem), produced by the activities of cork cambium (phellogen). The cells of this cork cambium produce a layer of cork to the outside and a layer of secondary cortex (phelloderm) to the inside. The walls of the cork cells become impregnated with a fatty material called **suberin**, which makes them impermeable to gases and water and causes the living contents to disappear. The suberised cells form a protective layer, preventing desiccation, mechanical injury and the entry of pathogenic organisms. At intervals, the cork cambium produces groups of loosely packed, thin-walled cells with no deposits of suberin. These groups of cells, which have large air spaces between them, form the lenticels and allow gaseous exchange to occur between the living cells of the stem and the environment. They appear as tiny slits or bumps on the bark of stems and twigs, easily visible with a hand lens.

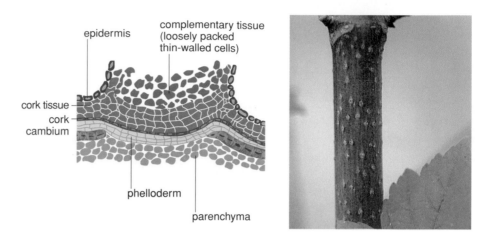

Figure 1.5 Vertical section through surface layers of woody twig showing lenticel structure (left) Photograph of a sycamore twig with lenticels (right)

Gas exchange in animals

Many groups of invertebrate animals, such as cnidarians and annelids, rely on simple diffusion of gases across their outer surface as a means of respiratory gas exchange. Their outer surface is moist and permeable to gases and functions as a gas exchange structure. In addition, their requirement for oxygen is relatively small. As organisms become larger and more complex, and their outer surface impermeable to gases, an efficient gas exchange system is necessary to supply the body tissues with oxygen and to remove carbon dioxide.

Gas exchange in insects

The exoskeleton of an insect is covered with a thin waxy layer, the epicuticle, which helps to prevent desiccation. The surface area of an insect is large in relation to its volume and these animals would readily dry out if not efficiently waterproofed. As a consequence of this waterproofing, the exoskeleton is impermeable to gases, so how do insects obtain the oxygen they need for respiration? Close examination of a large insect, such as a locust, reveals the presence of paired **spiracles**, or pores, in the exoskeleton. Spiracles may have valves, which are able to open and close. At rest, the spiracles are only opened occasionally, which helps to minimise water loss by evaporation and diffusion of water vapour through the spiracles. Each spiracle leads to a complex system of air-filled tubes, known as **tracheae** (singular trachea). Tracheae are strengthened by spirals of chitin, the taenidia, which prevent them from collapsing. As they divide and ramify through the tissues of the insect's body, the tracheae become progressively smaller in diameter, ending in blind-ended minute **tracheoles**. The end of each tracheole is enclosed in a long, invaginated cell about 0.1 μm in diameter and up to about 400 μm in length. The tip of each tracheole is branched and filled with fluid; exchange of oxygen and carbon dioxide occurs in solution between the tracheoles and body cells.

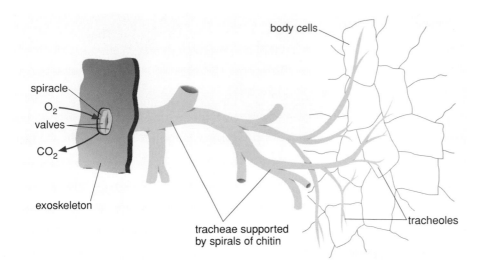

Figure 1.6 Spiracle and part of the tracheal system of an insect

At rest, small insects rely on simple diffusion of oxygen into their tracheal system and diffusion of carbon dioxide out. Closure of the spiracles both reduces water loss and helps to maintain a steep diffusion gradient for respiratory gases. When the spiracles are closed, the concentration of oxygen within the tracheal system decreases, resulting in a rapid influx of oxygen when the spiracles open. Conversely, carbon dioxide accumulates in the tracheae and rapidly diffuses out when the spiracles are opened.

When insects are more active, ventilation of the tracheal system is increased by muscular movement of the abdomen. Contraction of abdominal muscles results in the alternate compression and expansion of the tracheae, which increases the flow of air into and out of the tracheal system. In locusts, the thoracic and abdominal spiracles open and close alternately, resulting in a flow of air from front to back. This improves the efficiency of gas exchange as air is drawn into the thorax, where there is a high demand for oxygen by the flight muscles.

During periods of increased metabolic activity, lactate may begin to accumulate in the tissues. This decreases the tissue solute potential and water is drawn out of the tracheoles by osmosis. This brings air into closer contact with the respiring tissues and further increases the efficiency of gas exchange.

Gas exchange in mammals

The gas exchange system in mammals consists essentially of two major parts, a **conducting system**, for the conduction of inspired and expired gases, and an **interface** for the exchange of gases between air and blood. The conducting system begins with the nasal passages and continues as the **trachea**. The trachea divides to form the left and right primary or main **bronchi** which supply the lungs. Each primary bronchus divides repeatedly to form airways of progressively smaller diameter, the secondary bronchi supply air to the lobes of the lungs and the tertiary bronchi supply segments of each lobe. The tertiary bronchi divide into numerous smaller **bronchioles** which ultimately lead into the **alveoli**, where gas exchange occurs.

The structure of the airways conforms to a common basic plan. They consist essentially of a tube, lined with epithelium, containing variable amounts of cartilage and/or smooth muscle in the wall. The type of epithelium changes progressively from one type of airway to the next. In the trachea, the epithelium is described as pseudostratified columnar ciliated epithelium. This undergoes a progressive change to a simple cuboidal, non-ciliated type in the smallest airways. **Goblet cells**, which secrete mucus, are frequent in the epithelium of the trachea but they decrease in number and are absent in the terminal bronchioles.

Alveoli are the major sites of gas exchange. Each alveolus consists of a pocket-shaped structure 100 to 300 μm in diameter, open on one side, and lined with extremely flattened epithelial cells. It has been estimated that there are about 300 million alveoli in the human lungs, giving a considerable total surface area (40 to 60 m^2) for gas exchange. Each alveolus consists of three tissue components, epithelium, connective tissue and blood vessels. The epithelium consists of two cell types, referred to as Type I and Type II pneumocytes. Type I pneumocytes are large, extremely flattened cells and make up most of the alveolar wall. Type II pneumocytes secrete surfactant, a mixture of lipids and proteins, which helps to reduce the surface tension within each alveolus. Without this surfactant, the alveoli collapse and lung tissue loses its elastic recoil. The connective tissue forms a supporting layer beneath the epithelium and consists of fine fibres, such as collagen and elastin, together with cells known as fibroblasts. The blood vessels surrounding the alveoli are mainly capillaries, referred to as pulmonary capillaries, 7 to 10 μm in diameter, which form a dense network around each alveolus.

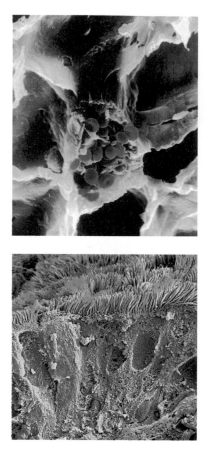

Figure 1.7 Photomicrographs to show the structures of alveoli (top) and respiratory epithelium (bottom)

The structure of each alveolus, with its surrounding capillaries, is well adapted for the process of gas exchange. Each alveolus is very thin-walled and there are millions of alveoli in each lung. The barrier for exchange of gases between alveolar air and the blood, known as the respiratory membrane, is of minimal thickness, less than 0.5 μm, which increases the efficiency of diffusion of gases.

The lungs have a number of defence mechanisms against inhaled microorganisms and small particles such as carbon in smoke. These defence mechanisms include filtration of inhaled air by the nose, the cough reflex and cilia and mucus within the larger airways. Cilia and mucus help to trap small particles in inspired air. Some particles, such as carbon, may reach the alveoli and are engulfed by wandering phagocytic cells known as **alveolar macrophages** or dust cells. These are derived from **monocytes** in blood, which migrate through blood vessel walls into various organs to become macrophages.

Ventilation in mammals

Pulmonary ventilation is the term given to the process of breathing, that is, the movement of air into and out of the respiratory system. Movement of air into the lungs is referred to as inspiration, while expiration is the movement of air out of the lungs.

Air moves into or out of the lungs as a result of differences in pressure between the atmosphere and alveolar air. When the atmospheric pressure (normally about 101 kPa, or 760 mm Hg) is greater than the pressure within the lungs, air will tend to flow down this pressure gradient and inspiration occurs. When the pressure in the lungs is greater than atmospheric pressure, air moves out of the lungs and into the atmosphere. The mechanism of pulmonary ventilation therefore depends on two gas pressure gradients, one in which the **intrapulmonary pressure** (pressure within the lungs) is lower than atmospheric pressure for inspiration to occur, and one in which the intrapulmonary pressure is higher than atmospheric pressure for expiration to occur. These pressure gradients are brought about by changes in the volume of the thorax which, in turn, are produced by contraction or relaxation of the respiratory muscles. The lungs follow these changes passively.

Inspiration

During inspiration, the volume of the thorax is increased by movements of the ribs upwards and outwards, and by contraction of the diaphragm. The diaphragm consists of striated muscle and a central tendinous area. It separates the thoracic and abdominal cavities. As the **diaphragm** contracts (when stimulated by the phrenic nerve), it flattens and descends, which increases the length of the thoracic cavity. Contraction of the **external intercostal muscles** pulls the anterior end of each rib upwards and outwards, increasing the diameter of the thorax. As the overall volume of the thorax increases, the intrapulmonary pressure decreases and inspiration occurs.

Expiration

Quiet expiration is brought about mainly by relaxation of the inspiratory muscles (the diaphragm and external intercostals), contraction of the **internal intercostal muscles,** and elastic recoil of lung tissue. The changes which occur are essentially the reverse of those described for inspiration, that is, the volume of the thorax decreases and, as a result, the intrapulmonary pressure increases, establishing a gradient to the atmosphere. Expiration then follows passively.

The intrapulmonary pressure therefore varies during inspiration and expiration. At the end of expiration during quiet breathing, the intrapulmonary pressure is the same as atmospheric pressure. As inspiration starts, the intrapulmonary pressure drops to about 0.4 kPa below atmospheric. During quiet expiration, the intrapulmonary pressure initially increases to about 0.4 kPa above atmospheric but returns to the atmospheric value by the time quiet expiration is completed.

It should be noted that the diaphragm and intercostal muscles are not the only muscles of ventilation. During quiet breathing, movement of the diaphragm accounts for about 75 per cent of the volume of air breathed. However, during forced inspiratory and expiratory efforts, many other muscles are used, including the abdominal muscles which contract during forced expiration. Forced expiratory efforts can greatly increase the intrapulmonary pressure. For example, forced expiration against a closed glottis (known as the Valsalva

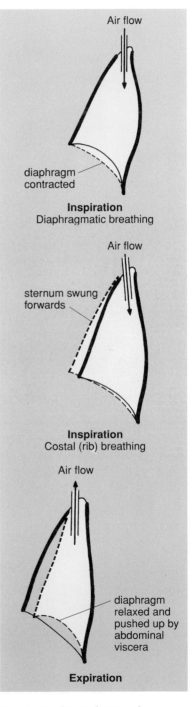

Figure 1.8 The mechanics of inspiration and expiration (see also Figures 1.9 and 1.10)

manœuvre) or when attempting to blow up a balloon, may raise the intrapulmonary pressure by 13 kPa or more.

The mechanisms of inspiration and expiration are summarised in Figures 1.9 and 1.10.

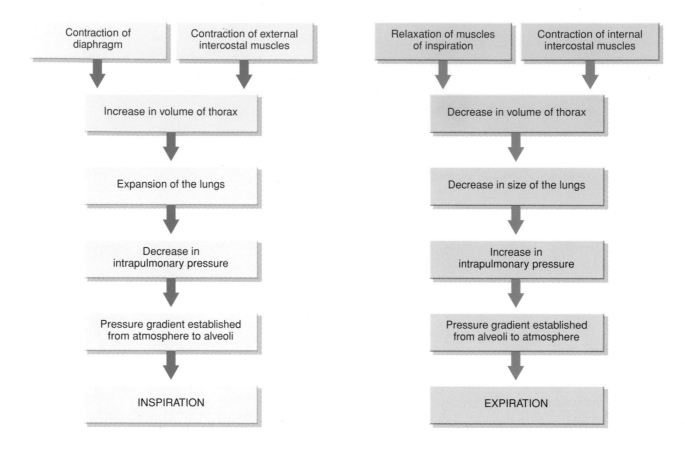

Figure 1.9 Mechanism of inspiration

Figure 1.10 Mechanism of expiration

Lung capacities

A **spirometer** (Figure 1.11) is a device which is used to measure and record the volumes of air inspired and expired. These volumes are of great importance as they can indicate whether or not adequate ventilation of the lungs is occurring so that there is normal exchange of oxygen and carbon dioxide between alveolar air and the pulmonary capillary blood.

The recording of the volumes of air inspired and expired, usually as a function of time, is referred to as a **spirogram** (Figure 1.12). The volume of air breathed in or out by an adult human during quiet breathing is about 500 cm^3. This is referred to as the resting **tidal volume** (TV). After a person has expired tidal air, it is possible to force more air out of the lungs. The maximum volume of air which can be forcibly expired after a tidal expiration is known as the **expiratory reserve volume** (ERV). The **inspiratory reserve volume** (IRV) is the volume of air which can be inspired over and above a tidal inspiration. Even after breathing out as far as possible, air remains in the

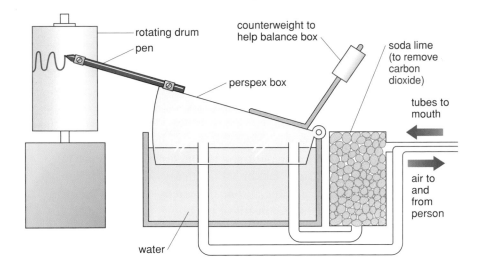

Figure 1.11 A spirometer

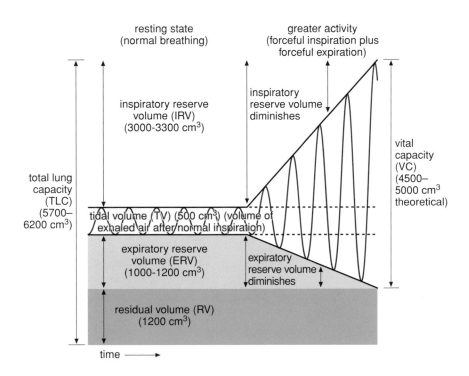

Figure 1.12 Major subdivisions of lung volumes

alveoli. This air, which keeps the alveoli partly inflated and enables gas exchange to continue between breaths, is known as the **residual volume** (RV).

The total of IRV + TV + ERV is known as the **vital capacity** (VC). The term capacity is used for the sum of two or more separate lung volumes. Vital capacity is related to the body size of a person and is usually about 2.6 dm^3 m^{-2} body surface area in males and 2.1 dm^3 m^{-2} in females. It is higher in swimmers and divers, and lower in older people and in diseases of the lungs

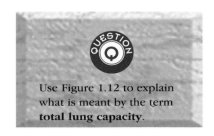

Use Figure 1.12 to explain what is meant by the term **total lung capacity**.

such as emphysema. Vital capacity is also affected by posture, being greater when the person is standing upright than when lying down.

Control of breathing

Breathing occurs due to the rhythmic activity of motor nerves which send impulses to the muscles of respiration. This rhythmic activity is entirely dependent on nerve impulses from the brain, as the muscles do not have any inherent rhythmic activity. Breathing is controlled by two interacting mechanisms, a voluntary system, situated in the cerebral cortex, and an automatic system situated in the pons and the medulla oblongata. The voluntary system is used to regulate breathing in activities such as speaking or playing a wind instrument, and the automatic system is used to regulate breathing to match the metabolic needs of the body.

The basic regular rhythm of breathing seems to be due to the activity of the **medullary rhythmicity centre**, situated in the medulla oblongata. This is turn consists of two interconnected centres, the **inspiratory centre** and the **expiratory centre**. Although the term centre is used, it is recognised that these actually consist of scattered groups of nerve cells within the brain stem. Nerve impulses from the inspiratory centre stimulate inspiration and impulses from the expiratory centre stimulate expiration. The medullary rhythmicity centre is similar to the pacemaker region of the heart (described in Chapter 2) as it has an inherent rhythm which can be modified by external influences.

The activity of the medullary rhythmicity centre is influenced by feedback information which comes from a number of sensors throughout the nervous system. Stimuli affecting the medullary rhythmicity centre can be divided into two groups, chemical and non-chemical. Chemical stimuli include the respiratory gases, oxygen and carbon dioxide, and changes in the pH of arterial blood. Non-chemical stimuli include feedback from, for example, stretch receptors located in the lungs. The effects of these types of stimuli are summarised below.

- **Oxygen** The precise role of oxygen in controlling breathing is not clear, but a decrease in arterial oxygen below about 9.3 kPa causes reflex stimulation of the inspiratory centre. An increase in arterial oxygen has little effect on breathing.
- **Carbon dioxide** Chemoreceptors in the medulla oblongata are sensitive to changes in the carbon dioxide content of arterial blood. A slight increase in carbon dioxide has a stimulating effect resulting in faster breathing with a greater volume of air moving in and out of the lungs each minute. This increases the removal of carbon dioxide via the lungs and brings the arterial blood carbon dioxide level back towards the normal range. Decreased carbon dioxide has the opposite effect, resulting in inhibition of the medullary rhythmicity centre and slower breathing. Breathing may stop entirely for a few seconds if arterial carbon dioxide drops to about 4.6 kPa (the normal range for arterial carbon dioxide is about 5.1 to 5.3 kPa).
- **pH of blood** A decrease in arterial blood pH (increase in acidity) has a stimulating effect on breathing and pulmonary ventilation increases.
- **Non-chemical stimuli** These include feedback from stretch receptors in the lungs which, as the lungs inflate, send inhibitory impulses to the

inspiratory centre, and impulses from sensory nerve endings in joints and tendons which help to control breathing during exercise.

Effects of exercise on pulmonary ventilation

Exercise can be considered to be of two types, moderate and very severe. These types of exercise have different effects on pulmonary ventilation. Moderate exercise is a type of exercise which can be maintained for long periods of time, such as walking briskly at 8 km per hour, or steady running. During moderate exercise, pulmonary ventilation increases steadily in proportion to the extent of the exercise, in order to supply sufficient oxygen to the active muscles. The exact reasons for this increase in ventilation are not clear, but are probably due to a number of factors including:

- nervous stimuli from higher centres in the brain and from sensory nerve endings in joints and muscles
- increased production of carbon dioxide
- production of lactate and consequent decrease in pH.

Table 1.2 shows the pulmonary ventilation of a man walking at different speeds.

Table 1.2 *Pulmonary ventilation of a man walking at different speeds*

Walking speed / km h^{-1}	Pulmonary ventilation / dm^3 min^{-1}
rest	10.0
3.2	19.0
4.8	25.0
6.4	37.0
8.0	60.0

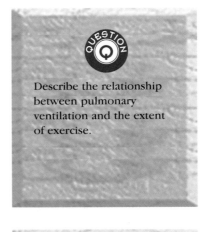

Describe the relationship between pulmonary ventilation and the extent of exercise.

Very severe exercise, such as running 100 metres at top speed, can only be maintained for a relatively short period of time. At the end of this exercise the runner is completely exhausted. Breathing remains much above the resting value for a prolonged period after the exercise is over. As an example, a man who ran 200 metres in 23.4 seconds took 27 minutes for the pulmonary ventilation to return to normal. After a 400 metre race, followed by vigorous gymnastics, the pulmonary ventilation returned to normal in 44 minutes. In the case of a 100 metre sprint, the runner may scarcely draw breath during the race, but will breathe heavily for some time afterwards.

Effects of training

The adaptations which are seen in the respiratory and cardiovascular systems and the muscles as a result of training depend on the nature of the training programme being followed. As an example, endurance training for prolonged exercise results in the following adaptations:

- an increase in the maximal blood supply to muscles and an increase in the maximal cardiac output (the volume of blood pumped out by the heart during one minute)
- an increase in the ability of the muscles to use oxygen
- more energy is derived from fat and less from carbohydrates
- less fatigue.

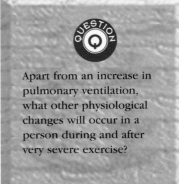

Apart from an increase in pulmonary ventilation, what other physiological changes will occur in a person during and after very severe exercise?

Effects of smoking on ventilation and gas exchange

Cigarette smoke contains a complex mixture of substances including nicotine, carbon monoxide, aromatic hydrocarbons, phenols and fatty acids. The hydrocarbons include tumour initiators, that is, substances which are able to start a malignant process – there is a linear relationship between the number of cigarettes smoked and the mortality risk from lung cancer. In addition to this increased risk of lung cancer, cigarette smoke has a number of other harmful effects including increasing the risk of **chronic bronchitis** and **emphysema**.

Cigarette smoke increases mucus production in the airways and makes the mucus more viscous. The smoke also paralyses the cilia which normally move mucus up the airways towards the pharynx. As a result, mucus tends to accumulate in the airways (chronic bronchitis), making infection almost inevitable. Bronchitis obstructs air flow and, as a result, there is inefficient gas exchange.

Emphysema is a destructive disease of the lungs due to damage to the connective tissue. The alveoli enlarge, their walls rupture and fuse into large, dilated, irregular air spaces. Destruction of lung tissue in this way is believed to be caused by the release of elastase, a proteolytic enzyme, by the alveolar macrophages and by neutrophils. Emphysema produces distended lungs with an appearance which has been described as similar to that of wire wool saucepan cleaners (Figure 1.13).

This destruction of lung tissue greatly decreases the surface area for gas exchange and as a result the blood may be poorly oxygenated, a condition referred to as **hypoxia**. This can cause serious distress and death from respiratory failure, heart failure or chest infection. There is no cure for emphysema, which is responsible for about 20 000 deaths per year in Great Britain.

Nitrogenous excretion in mammals

Urea is a product of metabolism. It is synthesised in the liver, as a result of the deamination of amino acids. Excess amino acids are neither stored in the body for future use in protein synthesis, nor are they excreted. Instead, they are converted to metabolic intermediates such as pyruvate and oxaloacetate and used in various metabolic pathways, including the synthesis of glucose. The first step in the breakdown of an amino acid is almost always the removal of the amino group, in the form of ammonia, which is then converted to urea by a series of reactions known as the **urea cycle**, or **ornithine cycle**. This cycle involves five enzyme-controlled reactions, two of which occur in the mitochondria and the rest in the cytoplasm. The overall reaction can be summarised as follows:

$$\text{ammonia} + \text{aspartate} \xrightarrow[\quad]{\text{ATP} \quad \text{ADP}} \text{urea} + \text{fumarate}$$

Urea is then secreted into the bloodstream and excreted in the urine.

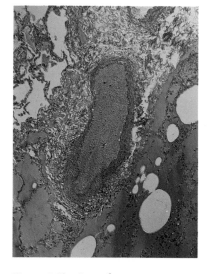

Figure 1.13   Part of an emphysematous lung, showing destruction of alveolar walls.

The mammalian kidney

The kidneys are major organs involved with homeostasis and have a number of functions including osmoregulation, maintenance of constant plasma pH and excretion of products of metabolism, such as urea and creatinine. They are situated on the posterior wall of the abdomen on either side of the vertebral column. Each human kidney is about 10 cm long, 5 cm wide and 3 cm thick and weighs about 100 g. In section, each kidney is seen to consist of an outer **cortex** and an inner **medulla** forming about twelve wedge-shaped structures, known as renal pyramids.

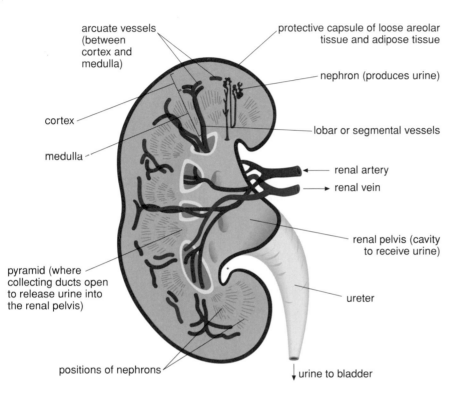

Figure 1.14 Internal structure of the kidney

The apex of each renal pyramid projects into a calyx. The calyces join together to form the renal pelvis which narrows as it leaves the kidney to become the **ureter**. The ureter is a narrow, muscular tube which conveys urine from the kidney to the bladder. The bladder acts as a reservoir for urine before it is expelled via the **urethra**.

Microscopic structure of the kidney

Each kidney consists of about one million microscopic functional units, the **nephrons**. Nephrons carry out the processes of osmoregulation and excretion and each consists of the following structures:

- renal corpuscle (Bowman's capsule and glomerulus)
- proximal convoluted tubule
- loop of Henle
- distal convoluted tubule
- collecting duct.

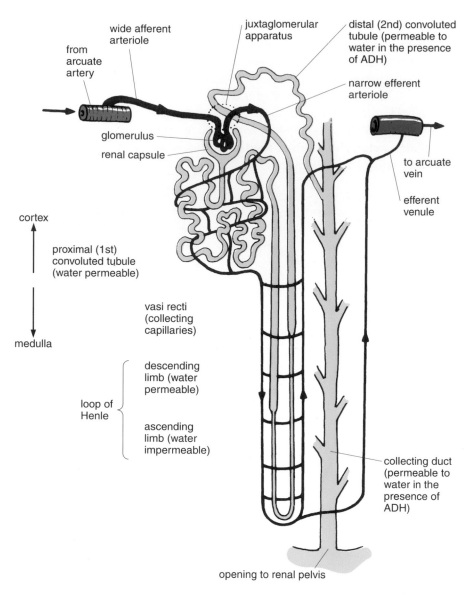

Figure 1.15 Structure of the nephron

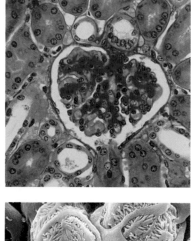

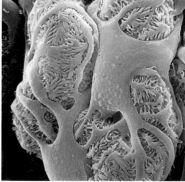

Figure 1.16 Light micrograph of renal corpuscle and scanning electronmicrograph showing podocytes.

The **Bowman's capsule** consists of a single layer of flattened epithelial cells and contains a tightly coiled network of capillaries, the **glomerulus**. These capillaries are surrounded by specialised epithelial cells, known as podocytes. Each podocyte has long cytoplasmic processes which in turn give rise to short foot processes, or pedicels. The pedicels are packed closely together, with narrow spaces between them of about 25 nm. These spaces are known as slit pores, through which ultrafiltration, the initial stage of urine formation, occurs.

The **proximal convoluted tubule** is the first part of the renal tubule. The wall of the proximal convoluted tubule consists of a single layer of cuboidal epithelial cells. These cells have a brush border of long microvilli, which almost completely fill the lumen of the tubule. The cytoplasm of the cells stains darkly due to a high density of organelles, chiefly mitochondria. These features are consistent with the cells having a high metabolic activity. The proximal convoluted tubule is the longest part of the nephron and, like the renal corpuscles, is situated in the cortex of the kidney.

The **loop of Henle** is the second part of the renal tubule and consists of a descending limb which arises in the cortex, followed by a sharp turn and an ascending limb which returns to the cortex. Cortical nephrons have loops of Henle which are restricted to the outer zone of the medulla, whilst juxtamedullary nephrons have longer loops of Henle which reach into the inner zone of the medulla before returning to the cortex.

The **distal convoluted tubule** is continuous with the ascending limb of the loop of Henle and consists of cuboidal epithelium with few, scattered, microvilli. In microscopic sections of kidney tissue, distal convoluted tubules can be distinguished from proximal convoluted tubules by the absence of a brush border, a larger, clearly defined lumen and more nuclei as the cells are smaller than those of the proximal convoluted tubule.

The **collecting duct** is a straight tubule which joins the distal convoluted tubules of several nephrons. Collecting ducts converge into larger ducts (known as the ducts of Bellini) which open into one of the calyces.

Functions of the kidney
The main functions of the kidney are to filter blood plasma and to excrete urine. The kidneys are the most important organs in the body for maintaining water, solute and pH balances. They are able to do this by varying the volume of water and the concentration of solutes which are lost in the urine, thus maintaining a balance of these substances in the body. If the kidneys fail, for example as a result of disease, homeostatic mechanisms also fail and, unless treated, the condition is inevitably fatal.

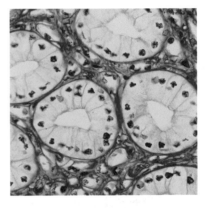

Figure 1.17 Collecting ducts t/s

Urine is formed in the nephron as a result of three major processes:
- ultrafiltration
- reabsorption
- secretion.

Ultrafiltration
Ultrafiltration is a physical process which occurs in the renal corpuscles. Large volumes of blood, approximately 1.2 dm^3, flow through the kidneys each minute. About one tenth of this volume is filtered through the glomerular capillaries and into the Bowman's capsule. The membranes of the glomerular capillaries are normally impermeable to solutes with a molecular mass over 70 000 and the filtrate is essentially a filtrate of plasma, containing virtually no protein and no cells. One reason for the rapid rate of filtration is the fact that the efferent arteriole has a smaller diameter than the afferent arteriole. This increases the resistance to blood flow out of the glomerulus and increases the pressure within the glomerular capillaries. It is this high blood pressure which provides the necessary force for ultrafiltration.

The total rate of formation of glomerular filtrate is about 170 to 180 dm^3 per day in humans, but the volume of urine produced is obviously very much less than this. It is clear that most of the filtrate must be reabsorbed as it passes through the renal tubules.

Reabsorption

Over two-thirds of the volume of filtrate entering the renal tubule from the Bowman's capsule is reabsorbed in the **proximal convoluted tubule**. Sodium ions (Na^+) are transported actively out of the lumen of the tubule and then diffuse into the capillaries which surround the proximal convoluted tubule (the peritubular capillaries). The microvilli on the epithelial cells greatly increase the surface area for the uptake of ions and other solutes. As sodium ions are taken up, an electrochemical gradient and negatively charged ions, such as chloride (Cl^-), and phosphate (PO_4^{3-}) are attracted to the positive ions. The concentration of ions in the capillaries therefore increases and this creates an osmotic gradient, causing water to move out of the proximal tubules by osmosis.

Reabsorption of glucose and amino acids also occurs in the proximal convoluted tubule. Reabsorption of glucose involves a special type of active transport, known as **sodium cotransport**. In this mechanism, both sodium ions and glucose bind to a carrier molecule in the epithelial cell surface membrane, which then passively transports both substances into the interior of the cell. Once inside the cell, the substances dissociate from the carrier molecule and diffuse to the basal end of the cell. Here, sodium is actively transported out of the cell and then diffuses into a peritubular capillary; glucose follows by passive diffusion. Normally, all of the glucose which has been filtered out of the glomerular capillaries is reabsorbed by the sodium cotransport mechanism and none is lost in the urine.

After the reabsorption of water, sodium ions, chloride ions, glucose and other solutes, the fluid remaining in the tubule has a relatively high concentration of urea. However, since the concentration of urea is higher in the tubule than in the surrounding capillaries, urea passively diffuses into the blood. Approximately half of the urea present in the tubular fluid is reabsorbed in this way.

Reabsorption in the proximal convoluted tubule can be summarised as follows:
- sodium ions are actively reabsorbed
- glucose and amino acids follow the reabsorption of sodium by means of the sodium cotransport mechanism
- chloride and other negatively charged ions are reabsorbed into the blood following an electrochemical gradient
- movement of solutes out of the tubule creates an osmotic gradient and water is reabsorbed by osmosis
- urea is reabsorbed by passive diffusion
- the volume of the filtrate is reduced by 75 to 80 per cent.

Control of water retention

The relatively small volume of filtrate remaining in the proximal convoluted tubule passes into the **loop of Henle**, a structure which enables the kidney to produce concentrated urine. The loop of Henle, and its surrounding capillaries, known as the vasa recta, form a **counter-current mechanism**. A counter-current structure is a set of parallel tubes in which the contents flow in opposite directions. In the loop of Henle, the contents of the descending limb flow in the opposite direction to the contents of the ascending limb. The structure of the loop of Henle, and the mechanism for the formation of concentrated urine are shown in Figure 1.18.

It appears that cells in the ascending limb of the loop of Henle actively pump chloride ions out of the filtrate and into the surrounding fluid. Since sodium ions follow the chloride ions, we often refer to active transport of sodium chloride. The descending limb is permeable to water, but impermeable to solutes. As the chloride pump has made the fluid surrounding the loop of Henle more concentrated, water is drawn out of the descending limb of the loop so that its contents become more concentrated. The fluid within the loop passing to the ascending limb has therefore become more concentrated, so more chloride ions are pumped out, more water is withdrawn from the descending limb, and so on. The water which is removed passes into the capillaries of the vasa recta (there is an osmotic gradient due to the plasma proteins). The fluid which flows from the ascending limb of the loop of Henle into the distal convoluted tubule has had sodium chloride removed from it and its concentration is lower than that of blood plasma. However, although the concentration of sodium chloride is low, the concentration of urea is relatively high. Cells in the collecting duct are permeable to both water and urea. Remember that the concentration of sodium chloride in the fluid surrounding the loop of Henle and the collecting duct is high and therefore water is drawn out of the collecting duct, by osmosis. As water moves out, the urea becomes more concentrated and moves out of the collecting duct by diffusion. The urea contributes to the osmotic effect and the high concentration of solutes in the medulla, derived from both urea and sodium chloride, enables the kidney to produce a concentrated urine.

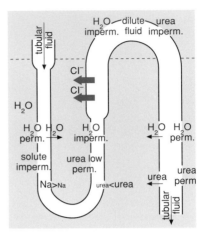

Figure 1.18 The concentrating mechanism in the loop of Henle

The ability of the mammalian kidney to produce a concentrated urine is closely related to the length of the loop of Henle. Desert mammals, such as the gerbil, *Meriones* sp., produce highly concentrated urine and have nephrons with exceptionally long loops of Henle. Indeed, so efficient is the mechanism for reabsorption of water that some desert rodents can live indefinitely on dry food and never need to drink.

The main functions of the loop of Henle are summarised below:
- water is reabsorbed from the tubular fluid in the descending limb
- sodium and chloride ions are reabsorbed in the ascending limb
- reabsorption of sodium and chloride ions creates a high solute concentration in the medulla.

The **distal convoluted tubule**, like the proximal convoluted tubule, also reabsorbs sodium ions, but in much smaller amounts. Cells in the distal convoluted tubule are relatively impermeable to water, but their permeability is markedly increased by **antidiuretic hormone** (ADH), which is secreted by the posterior pituitary gland. ADH is involved in the regulation of water loss by the kidney. It acts on cells of the distal convoluted tubule and collecting duct and causes them to become more permeable to water. The more ADH present, the more water will be reabsorbed and, consequently, the more concentrated the urine will be.

EXCHANGES WITH THE ENVIRONMENT

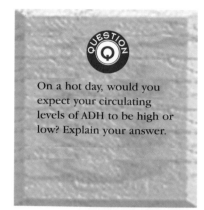

QUESTION

On a hot day, would you expect your circulating levels of ADH to be high or low? Explain your answer.

The secretion of ADH depends on the concentration of solutes in plasma and extracellular fluids. If this is raised by about one per cent, the secretion of ADH is increased. If the concentration decreases, ADH secretion will also decrease. Changes in the concentration of plasma and extracellular fluid are detected by specialised nerve cells, known as **osmoreceptors**, situated in the hypothalamus. Increased activity of the osmoreceptors results in an increased ADH secretion and, therefore, increased reabsorption of water.

Kidney failure, the kidney machine and transplantation

Kidney failure, or renal failure, simply means the failure of the kidneys to filter blood plasma and to form urine. Kidney failure can be classified as either **chronic** or **acute**. Acute kidney failure is a sudden decrease in kidney function, characterised by a very small urine volume and a rapid increase in nitrogenous waste products, such as urea, in the blood. Acute kidney failure can be caused by various factors which result in a change in blood pressure or affect glomerular filtration. Such factors include haemorrhage, severe burns and acute glomerulonephritis (a disease which affects the glomeruli). If the cause of acute kidney failure is treated, the patient usually makes a rapid and complete recovery.

Chronic kidney failure is a slow, progressive condition which results from the gradual loss of nephrons. There are many diseases which may result in loss of nephron function, including infections, glomerulonephritis and autoimmune disorders. Chronic kidney failure is described as passing through three stages, as outlined below:

- **Stage 1** Some nephrons are lost, others compensate by enlarging.
- **Stage 2** During this stage also known as renal insufficiency, the remaining healthy nephrons begin to fail and the concentration of blood urea starts to climb.
- **Stage 3** In the final stage of kidney failure, known as uraemia, or uraemic syndrome, fluids are retained in the body. Unless a kidney machine is used, or a new kidney is transplanted, this complete loss of kidney function will cause death.

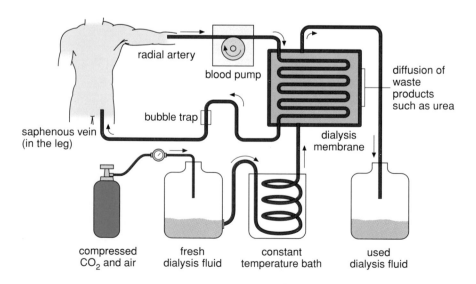

Figure 1.19 Principle of a kidney machine, which uses the process of dialysis to remove waste products from the patient's blood. A dialysis membrane separates small molecules from large particles.

The kidney machine

This is a mechanical device which uses the principle of **dialysis** to separate waste products from the blood. This process, known as haemodialysis, uses an artificial membrane to separate large particles, such as blood cells and proteins, from small molecules such as urea and other waste products. For a patient with complete kidney failure, two or three treatments are required each week. A diagram of a kidney machine is shown in Figure 1.19.

Kidney transplantation

This involves transferring a healthy kidney from one person, known as the **donor**, into a patient whose kidneys have failed, the **recipient**. The transplanted kidney then takes over the functions of the failed kidneys. One problem with this procedure is the tendency of the recipient's immune system to reject a transplanted organ as foreign tissue, causing what is known as rejection syndrome. This can be prevented by either tissue typing to match as closely as possible the antigens of the host with those of the recipient, or by using immunosuppressive drugs, such as cyclosporin, to suppress the ability of the immune system to attack foreign antigens in the donated tissue.

The number of kidney transplants carried out in the United Kingdom in 1996 was 1646 (UK Transplant Support Service Authority), but there is a shortage of suitable donors.

Ventilation movements in an insect

Introduction

The aim of this practical is to measure and record the ventilation rate in an insect, and to investigate some of the factors which influence this rate. Locusts are suitable insects to use for this investigation and will be unharmed by the procedure.

Materials

- Adult (or 5th stage hopper) locust
- Transparent plastic 20 cm^3 syringe. If syringes are not available, a boiling tube fitted with a cotton wool plug and a drinking straw makes a suitable alternative
- Cotton wool
- Rubber or PVC tubing
- Stop clock
- Access to a refrigerator

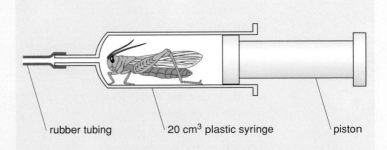

rubber tubing   20 cm^3 plastic syringe   piston

Figure 1.20 Apparatus for investigating ventilation in a locust

EXCHANGES WITH THE ENVIRONMENT

Method

1 Place a locust in a plastic syringe as shown in Figure 1.20. Carefully insert the piston and push this in gently so that the locust cannot move.
2 Observe the locust and count the number of ventilation movements of the abdomen which occur during 30 seconds. Record the results of three successive counts.
3 Attach a length of tubing to the syringe, remove the piston and replace with a plug of cotton wool so that the locust cannot escape. Breathe gently out through the tube for 10 to 15 seconds, then count ventilation movements as in step 2.
4 Remove the cotton wool plug and replace with the piston. Carefully move the piston in and out to replace the air in the syringe with fresh air.
5 Count and record the ventilation movements as before, then place the syringe in a refrigerator at about 5°C for 15 minutes. Finally, count and record the ventilation movements.

Results and discussion

1 Record all your results in a table.
2 Formulate a hypothesis about the composition of the air and the ventilation rate of the locust.
3 Which factors changed when you breathed onto the locust?
4 How could you reduce these variables?
5 Explain the effect of reducing the temperature on the ventilation rate.

Use of a simple respirometer

Introduction

A respirometer is used to measure either the volume of carbon dioxide produced or the volume of oxygen consumed by living organisms. There are many different types of respirometer which vary in complexity from a simple respirometer to elaborate and sensitive types which can be used to measure minute volumes of gas.

One of the problems in respirometry is that gas volumes are influenced by changes in temperature and pressure. Therefore, it is important to control and make allowances for these variables if meaningful results are to be obtained. The respirometer shown in Figure 1.21 consists of two tubes; one contains the respiring material or organisms, the other acts as a thermobarometer and compensates for small changes in temperature or pressure. If the air in this tube expands or contracts it will oppose similar changes in the respiration tube. Differences in the level of the manometer fluid are therefore due only to respiratory activity.

If we wish to measure the volume of oxygen used in respiration, the respirometer contains a substance which absorbs carbon dioxide as it is produced. The decrease in gas volume in the respirometer will therefore be equal to the volume of oxygen used. Substances which absorb carbon dioxide include potassium hydroxide and soda lime.

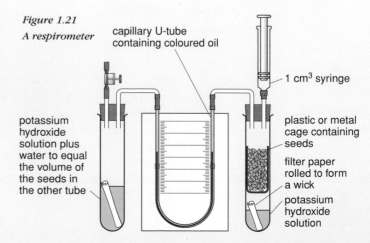

Figure 1.21
A respirometer

capillary U-tube containing coloured oil

1 cm³ syringe

potassium hydroxide solution plus water to equal the volume of the seeds in the other tube

plastic or metal cage containing seeds

filter paper rolled to form a wick

potassium hydroxide solution

CORROSIVE

CAUTION:

Great care should be exercised when using these substances – potassium hydroxide in particular is corrosive – gloves and safety glasses should be worn when handling it.

Materials

- Respirometer
- Germinating barley grains or pea seeds
- potassium hydroxide solution, 15 per cent w/v
- Filter paper
- Manometer fluid (Brodie's fluid)
- Water bath and thermometer

Method

1 Carefully pour about 5 cm^3 of potassium hydroxide solution into each tube of the respirometer, or add about 5 g of soda lime granules. If you use potassium hydroxide solution, be careful not to allow it to touch the sides of the tubes. If you spill potassium hydroxide solution onto your skin or clothes, wash it off immediately with cold water.

2 Fill the wire or plastic basket with germinating seeds and place in one vessel, ensuring that the seeds do not come into contact with the potassium hydroxide solution.

3 Fill another basket with an equivalent volume of glass beads, and place in the other tube.

4 Carefully draw Brodie's fluid into the manometer tube so that it comes about half-way up the scale on either side. It is very important that there are no air bubbles in the manometer fluid.

5 Remove the syringe and screw clip, then connect the manometer to both tubes.

6 Stand the respirometer in a water bath at 20 °C with the manometer outside the water bath.

7 Leave the respirometer for at least five minutes to equilibrate. Adjust the piston of the syringe so that it is at about the 0.5 cm^3 mark, then connect to the respirometer as shown in the diagram. Close the screw clip.

8 Use the syringe to adjust the manometer fluid so that the levels are equal on both sides.

9 Record the positions of the syringe piston, the level of the manometer fluid and the time.

10 Record the level of the manometer fluid at suitable time intervals. How frequently you need to take readings will depend on the respiration rate of the organisms you are using.

11 When the manometer fluid reaches the end of the scale, the syringe can be used to return the fluid to its original level.

12 Repeat the experiment at 30 °C and 40 °C, recording your results carefully each time.

13 When you have completed the experiment, record the mass of living material.

Results and discussion

1 Plot a graph of manometer readings against time, for each set of results at a particular temperature.

2 If the graph is a straight line, what does it indicate about the rate of respiration at a particular temperature?

3 You can use the syringe to calibrate the respirometer and then calculate the respiration rate. This should be expressed as mm^3 of oxygen used per milligram of living material per hour (mm^3 oxygen mg^{-1} hr^{-1}).

4 What effect did increasing the temperature have on the respiration rate? How could this effect be expressed quantitatively?

EXCHANGES WITH THE ENVIRONMENT

Practical: Measurement of vital capacity

Introduction

The vital capacity (maximum volume of air which can be expired following maximal inspiration) of a person can be measured simply by using a suitably calibrated glass bell jar, supported in a sink of water.

Materials

- Large (5 dm^3) calibrated bell jar
- Wide diameter rubber or PVC tubing
- Suitable supports for the bell jar

<table>
<tr><td>

estimated vital capacities

For males,
2.6 dm^3 m^{-2}
body surface area

For females,
2.1 dm^3 m^{-2}
body surface area

</td></tr>
</table>

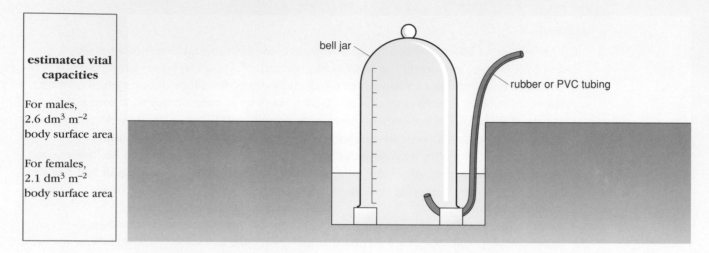

Figure 1.22 Method for determining the vital capacity

Method

1 First calibrate the bell jar by inverting it and pouring in known volumes of water. Use a marker pen to graduate the jar.
2 Fill the jar and invert into a large sink filled with water. Support the jar on suitable blocks.
3 If available, use a standing waste so that the sink is about two-thirds full.
4 Each student then uses the tubing and, following maximal inspiration, exhales as far as possible into the jar.
5 The vital capacity can then be recorded.

Results and discussion

NB: When investigating physiological parameters, it should be noted that there is always variation from person to person. The data should therefore be interpreted with care as there are many factors which can influence the results obtained.

1 Record class results in a suitable table.
2 Is there a consistent difference between the vital capacity of males and females ? If so, can this be quantified?
3 Investigate the effect of posture on vital capacity and suggest reasons for the results.
4 If available, use a surface area nomogram to determine your body surface area and, using the relationship in the margin above, calculate your estimated vital capacity. Suggest reasons for any differences there may be.

Transport systems

The need for transport systems

In addition to the exchange of materials between an organism and its environment, which was discussed at the beginning of Chapter 1, there is the need for materials to be transported within the organism. Oxygen and nutrients need to be transported from their place of uptake to the respiring cells; carbon dioxide and other waste products must be removed. In green plants, water and mineral ions needed for photosynthesis are taken up by the roots and need to be transported to the leaves where light and carbon dioxide are absorbed. The resulting organic compounds must be transported away from their site of synthesis to other regions for use in metabolic activities or for storage. The transport system in flowering plants consists of the vascular tissue, composed of xylem and phloem.

In mammals, absorption of the digested food takes place in the small intestine, from where it is transported to the liver and then to the respiring cells. Absorption of oxygen and removal of carbon dioxide occurs in the lungs, so a transport system is needed to deliver oxygen to the respiring cells and to remove carbon dioxide.

In many small organisms, efficient internal transport of all materials can be achieved through diffusion or active transport, because the distances involved are small and, where diffusion is concerned, the concentration gradients are favourable. In larger organisms, the distances between the different parts are too large and these processes are too slow. In addition, larger animals tend to be more active than smaller animals, leading to greater metabolic activity and a consequent need for a faster supply of oxygen and nutrients to the respiring cells.

In the Kingdom Animalia, Phylum Cnidaria, an adequate supply of oxygen can be supplied to respiring cells by diffusion alone. For example, in *Hydra*, a cnidarian frequently found clinging to water plants in freshwater habitats, the body wall consists of two layers of cells, the ectoderm and the endoderm. Water enters the body cavity and circulates around so both the layers of cells are in contact with the water, from which oxygen is obtained by diffusion.

In the Phylum Platyhelminthes, the body consists of three layers of cells: the ectoderm on the outside, the mesoderm in the middle and the endoderm surrounding the gut cavity. These animals, though much more complex than *Hydra*, do not have a special transport system as their bodies are flattened and the gut, when present, is much branched. In *Planaria*, a free-living flatworm of the Class Turbellaria, gaseous exchange occurs by diffusion over the external surface of the organism and the products of digestion can diffuse from the much branched gut to all the respiring cells. Other members of this phylum, such as the flukes (Class Trematoda) and the tapeworms (Class Cestoda) are internal parasites of vertebrates and do not possess a gut. They absorb their nutrients by diffusion over their body surface.

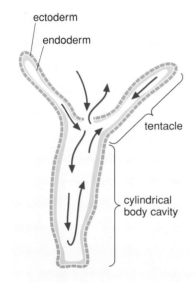

Figure 2.1 Hydra *showing two-layered body wall. The arrows indicate the circulation of water.*

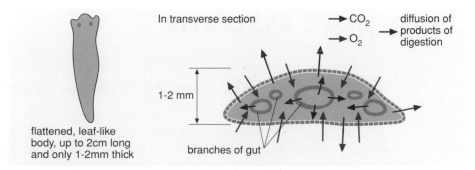

Figure 2.2 Planaria *showing flattened body and diffusion paths of oxygen and nutrients*

In all the other animal phyla, internal transport systems are present. These usually consist of a fluid, blood, which is pumped around the body by one or more muscular structures called hearts. The blood is either pumped through a system of internal spaces, as in the open circulation of arthropods and molluscs, or through a continuous system of closed tubes, blood vessels, in the closed circulation of vertebrates.

In the open circulatory system of an insect, the blood leaves the head region and enters spaces called **sinuses**, where it bathes the body organs. The blood is under relatively low pressure and there are valves which, together with waves of contraction of the muscular heart, maintain the movement of the blood back towards the head region, where the circulation starts again.

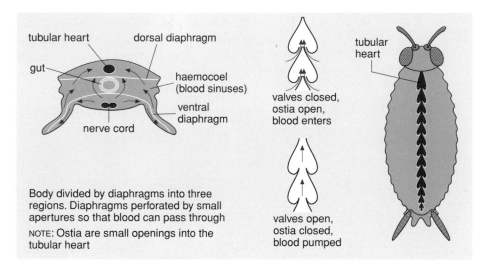

Figure 2.3 Circulatory system in an insect

There are two types of closed circulatory system:
 • **single circulations** – present in fish, in which blood is pumped from the heart to the gills, then to the rest of the body before being returned to the heart
 • **double circulations** – typical of mammals, where blood is pumped from the heart to the lungs and back to the heart in a pulmonary circulation, followed by the systemic circulation in which the blood is pumped from the heart to the body organs and back to the heart.

The concept of mass flow

Mass flow, alternatively known as bulk flow, is thought to account for the long-distance transport of fluids in living organisms. The fluid, together with any substances dissolved or suspended in it, moves in bulk, in response to a pressure gradient. This can be illustrated by considering the flow of liquid up a drinking straw. The person sucking the drinking straw lowers the pressure at the top end, which causes the liquid to move from a high pressure to a lower pressure. In plants, movement of water and mineral ions up the xylem from the roots to the leaves is largely brought about by the evaporation of water from the leaves. This causes a lowering of the pressure at the top of the plant and does not involve metabolic energy.

Transport in flowering plants

In flowering plants, water, mineral ions and organic solutes are transported from their sites of uptake or synthesis to where they are used or, in the case of water, removed. This transport can occur over short distances from cell to cell, or over greater distances involving the vascular tissue, which is specialised for conducting water and solutes. Movement of substances from cell to cell may involve diffusion or active transport, see *Cell Biology and Genetics*.

Movement of water

Water moves through a plant from the root hairs, where uptake occurs, through the root to the stem and leaves, where most of it is lost as water vapour in the process of **transpiration**. The continual evaporation of water from the aerial parts of the flowering plant into the atmosphere is due to a water potential gradient which exists between the soil and the atmosphere. The root hairs are in contact with the soil water, which has a high water potential, and the leaves and stems are exposed to the atmosphere, which has a much lower water potential. Consequently, there is a tendency for water to be drawn through and lost from the plant. This movement of water is a passive process. As water evaporates from the aerial parts of the plant, it changes from a liquid to a vapour. This change of state requires heat energy, referred to as the **latent heat of vaporisation**.

The movement of water into and between living cells occurs by osmosis, but the long-distance transport occurs by mass flow, where the water and solute molecules move together and in one direction, due to differences in pressure. The long-distance transport of water and mineral ions, from roots to shoots, occurs in the **xylem tissue** and because it occurs while the plant is transpiring it is referred to as the **transpiration stream**. The uptake of water by the root hairs occurs by osmosis and this process, together with details of root structure, is described fully in Chapter 3 of *The Organism and the Environment, Second Edition*.

Water vapour may be lost from three sites on the aerial parts of the plant: the cuticle, the stomata on leaves, flowers and herbaceous stems and the lenticels on woody stems. Most of the water vapour loss occurs through the stomata, which are open during the day allowing for the exchange of gases in photosynthesis. Evaporation through the cuticle, which accounts for about 10 per cent of the total water loss, will vary with its thickness. The amount of

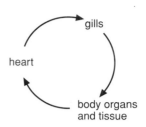

Fish: single circulation

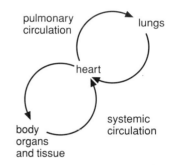

Mammal: double circulation

Figure 2.4 Fish and mammal circulation to show differences between single and double circulatory systems

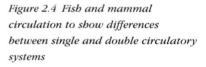

ψ in atmosphere −30 000 KPa (most negative)

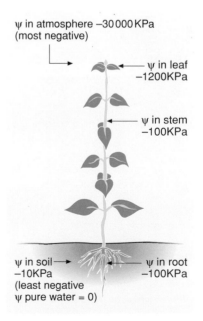

ψ in leaf −1200 KPa

ψ in stem −100 KPa

ψ in soil −10 KPa (least negative ψ pure water = 0)

ψ in root −100 KPa

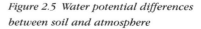

Figure 2.5 Water potential differences between soil and atmosphere

evaporation through the lenticels is very small, but this is the main way in which water is lost from the stems of deciduous trees after leaf fall.

Stomata

Stomata are pores in the epidermis of leaves, flowers and herbaceous stems through which exchange of gases occurs. They are most frequent on leaves and may occur on both surfaces, but are more common on the lower (abaxial) surface. Surrounding each pore are two **guard cells**, which control the size of the opening by changes in their turgidity. The guard cells are usually kidney-shaped, but in grasses they appear dumb-bell-shaped. The adjacent epidermal cells are often arranged in a characteristic pattern and referred to as **subsidiary cells**. The guard cells are different from the rest of the epidermal cells in that they contain chloroplasts, they are not linked to adjacent cells by plasmodesmata and their walls are unevenly thickened. The part of the cellulose cell wall which borders the pore is thicker, and also less elastic, than the opposite wall. As water is taken into the guard cells, increasing their turgidity, they become more curved and the pore between them opens wider. When the guard cells lose turgidity, they become less curved and the pore closes.

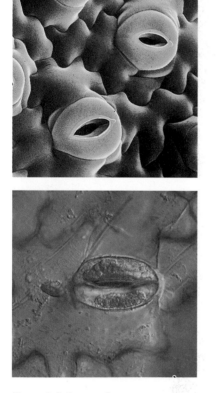

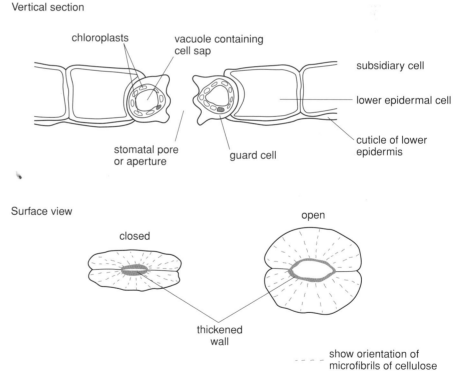

Vertical section

chloroplasts

vacuole containing cell sap

subsidiary cell

lower epidermal cell

stomatal pore or aperture

guard cell

cuticle of lower epidermis

Surface view

closed

open

thickened wall

- - - - - show orientation of microfibrils of cellulose

Figure 2.6 Stomatal structure. Photographs show (upper) scanning electron micrograph of open stomata on the leaf of a tobacco plant (Nicotiana tabacum) *and (lower) light micrograph of closed stoma on the leaf of a broad bean* (Vica faba)

The chemiosmotic mechanism of stomatal opening and closing

Concurrent with the opening of a stoma, there is a considerable increase in the concentration of solutes in the guard cells, causing the water potential to become more negative (lower). This causes water to move in to the cells and the turgor pressure rises. Investigations of the concentrations of different ions in the guard cells of open and closed stomata have shown that as the stoma opens, there is a steep rise in the concentration of potassium ions and chloride ions. The first stage in this process is thought to involve the removal of hydrogen ions from the guard cells due to the action of a **proton pump**. An electrochemical gradient builds up across the guard cell membrane and the potassium ions diffuse in passively. Due to the active removal of hydrogen ions, the pH inside the guard cell rises, whilst that outside decreases.

In order that the intracellular pH is controlled, there is a second stage to the process which involves the inward diffusion of chloride ions, either as a result of the change in pH or linked with hydrogen ion uptake. In addition, there is an increase in the amount of malate in the guard cell. It is thought that the increase in pH activates the enzyme phosphoenolpyruvate carboxylase (PEP carboxylase), which catalyses the fixation of carbon dioxide to produce oxaloacetic acid. The oxaloacetic acid can be reduced to malic acid which dissociates, providing malate ions, to balance the potassium ions, and hydrogen ions for the proton pump. Starch stored in the guard cells provides the pyruvate, which is first converted to phosphoenolpyruvate before carbon dioxide fixation occurs.

Some plants, such as onions (*Allium cepa*), do not store starch in their guard cells, so malate ions do not accumulate. In such cases, it is thought that the uptake of chloride ions alone is responsible for maintaining the balance.

According to this suggested mechanism for guard cell behaviour, when the proton pump stops, potassium and chloride ions diffuse out along electrochemical gradients. It has been possible to show that the concentrations of these ions increase in the surrounding epidermal cells as the stomata close. The levels of malate also decrease, probably due to outward diffusion as well as metabolism.

The energy source for the proton pump is ATP and it is suggested that this may come from three sources:
• photophosphorylation by the chloroplasts in the guard cells
• oxidative phosphorylation
• a separate photosystem triggered by blue light.

Photophosphorylation and the separate photosystem require light, but oxidative phosphorylation can operate in the absence of light, so any of these three sources may be in use depending on the circumstances.

A number of factors influence the opening and closing of the stomata. These include the prevailing light conditions, the supply of water to the plant and the supply of respiratory substrates. In plants that are well supplied with water, the stomata open at dawn and close at dusk and this pattern appears to be controlled by light and the amount of carbon dioxide in the intercellular spaces of the leaves. Photosynthesis is initiated by light and as soon as the process begins, there will be a decrease in the amount of carbon dioxide in the leaf. It has been observed that low concentrations of carbon dioxide in the

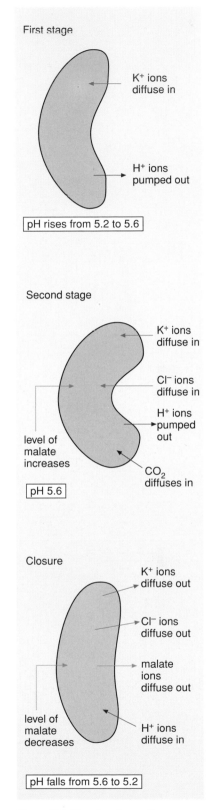

Figure 2.7 The chemiosmotic mechanism of stomatal opening

leaves promote stomatal opening and high concentrations bring about stomatal closure. Although it has been possible to show that the guard cells are sensitive to different levels of carbon dioxide, the precise mechanism of how this might cause stomatal opening is not known.

It is quite common for stomatal closure to occur around midday in leafy trees. When air temperatures are high and the humidity is low, transpiration is high and water loss may exceed water uptake, so this pattern of closure could avoid air locks in the xylem vessels impeding the transpiration stream. This pattern of closure appears to be controlled by external factors, but if wilting is imminent, the stomata close rapidly. Under these circumstances, the decrease in turgor of the leaf cells triggers the synthesis of a plant growth inhibitor, **abscisic acid** (ABA), in the chloroplasts. If the level of ABA is sufficiently high, it affects the cell surface membrane of the guard cells, preventing the proton pump from operating and bringing about closure of the stomata. As soon as more water is available to the plant, the ABA is broken down.

The transpiration stream

Most of the water lost by a plant is in the form of water vapour. Evaporation occurs from the cellulose cell walls of the mesophyll cells into the intercellular spaces, from where it diffuses out through the stomata, from a high water potential inside the leaf to a lower water potential outside. In dicotyledonous plants, there are usually larger numbers of stomata on the lower surfaces of leaves than on the upper, but in monocotyledonous plants like the grasses, with long, narrow leaves, the stomata are evenly distributed on both leaf surfaces.

Water reaches the mesophyll cells from the xylem of the vascular bundles in the leaf veins. At their extreme ends, these veins consist of little more than one or two vessels with little lignification, so water can easily pass to the adjacent mesophyll via the apoplast, symplast or vacuolar pathways. These pathways are described in *The Organism and the Environment, Second Edition* and summarised here in Figure 2.8.

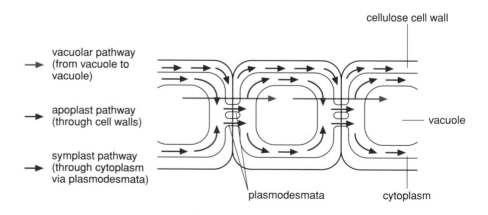

Figure 2.8 Apoplast, symplast and vacuolar pathways of water supplying mesophyll cells

The cohesion–tension theory

Removal of water from the xylem in the veins of the leaf creates a pulling force which draws water through the vascular tissue from the roots to the stem in continuous columns. The maintenance of these continuous columns is due to the structure of the xylem tissue and the properties of water. The **cohesion–tension theory** was put forward to account for the movement of water through the plant, bearing in mind the nature of the xylem tissue, the large quantities of water involved and the distances over which the transport was required.

In the xylem tissue, **tracheids** and **vessels** are the main conducting cells. Tracheids are dead, elongated cells with lignified walls and tapered ends. Their walls are pitted, ie possess unlignified areas consisting of just the middle lamella and the remains of the primary cell wall. Vessels consist of columns of cells, called vessel segments, joined end to end, each with a lignified, pitted wall and no cell contents. The end walls of these segments break down during development, forming a long tube. Both tracheids and vessels have strong, rigid walls, which are able to withstand tension, and are small in diameter (see Figure 5.6). There is an attraction between the water molecules and the walls of these cells (**adhesion**) and the water molecules stick to the walls. There are also strong forces between the water molecules (**cohesion**), which play a major role in maintaining the continuity of the water columns in the tissue.

Water columns under such tension are sometimes broken through wounding, entry of air or if the pressure drops. Water will vaporise and the affected vessel will develop an air bubble, which blocks water movement. Due to the presence of pits, enabling the sideways movement of water, the affected vessel may be bypassed. The pit membrane gets pushed against the pit aperture and prevents the air bubble passing from one vessel to another.

Water movement in the xylem can be affected to some extent by **root pressure**. If the shoot of a plant is cut off close to the ground, sap will exude from the xylem tissue of the stump. This process occurs because ions are still being taken up actively by the roots and there is also osmotic uptake of water into the xylem. It can be demonstrated that a positive hydrostatic pressure of about 150 kPa may be generated by root pressure, so although it could not account for all the water movement in the xylem, it may have a contributory role. It has been suggested that air bubbles in the xylem of herbaceous plants may be removed by root pressure occurring when transpiration ceases at night.

Factors affecting the rate of transpiration

The rate of transpiration can be affected by environmental factors and also by a number of structural or internal features of the plants. The environmental factors include:
- light
- temperature
- humidity
- air movements.

Bordered pit in xylem

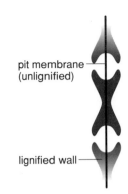

pit membrane
(unlignified)

lignified wall

Flow of water

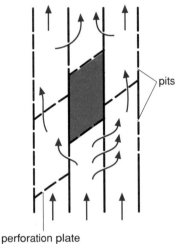

pits

perforation plate
of vessel segment

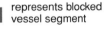 represents blocked
vessel segment

Figure 2.9 Structure of a pit (top) and sideways flow of water through the xylem (bottom)

Light affects the rate of transpiration because the size of the stomatal aperture is controlled by light. As stomata open in the morning , the rate of transpiration increases, decreasing at dusk when the stomata close. Some transpiration may occur through the cuticle, referred to as **cuticular transpiration**, when stomata are closed.

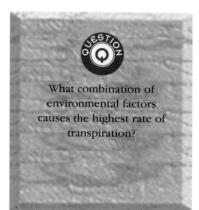

What combination of environmental factors causes the highest rate of transpiration?

The rate of transpiration increases with an increase in **temperature**, because higher temperatures cause water to evaporate more rapidly from the cell walls of the mesophyll tissue. This increases the concentration of water vapour molecules in the air spaces in the leaf. Warmer temperatures also lower the humidity of the air outside the leaf, thus increasing the difference in water potential between the leaf and the atmosphere, so water will diffuse out more rapidly.

The water vapour pressure, or **humidity**, of the atmosphere has an effect on the rate of transpiration. If the humidity is low, the air is relatively dry and there is a steeper diffusion gradient between the external atmosphere and the atmosphere inside the leaf, so the rate of transpiration is higher. If the humidity is high, the air is more saturated with water vapour molecules and the converse applies.

In still air, 'shells' of air saturated with water vapour molecules are built up around the leaves, with the effect of reducing the rate of transpiration as the diffusion gradients are less steep. Any air movement can disturb these shells, moving the water vapour molecules away from the surface of the leaves and thus creating steeper diffusion gradients.

Internal factors which affect the transpiration rate include
- the surface area of the leaf: the greater the surface area, the higher the rate of transpiration
- the thickness of the cuticle: a thick cuticle reduces the rate of cuticular transpiration
- stomatal density: the greater the number of stomata per unit area of leaf, the greater the rate of transpiration.

What additional features are typical of the leaves of xerophytes?

Many plants living in dry conditions show adaptations which have the effect of reducing the rate of transpiration and thus conserving water. Such plants are referred to as **xerophytes** and their adaptations as **xeromorphic**. The adaptations shown by some xerophytic plants are described in Chapter 3 of *The Organism and the Environment, Second Edition*.

Movement of nutrients
Uptake of mineral ions, their transport and circulation

Mineral ion uptake in flowering plants takes place at the roots, the ions being absorbed along with water from the soil solution. Small amounts of ions can be also absorbed by the leaves from rainwater. Most of the uptake occurs in the root hair region of young roots, where there is a large surface area available, for efficient uptake. The uptake of most ions is an active process, against a concentration gradient, as the majority of ions needed are present in higher concentrations in the root cells than they are in the soil solution. Ions may diffuse in passively by mass flow through the apoplast, if their concentration outside the roots is higher than their concentration within the cells. This situation occurs in the case of calcium ions, which are nearly always in higher concentrations in the soil solution than in the root cells.

Active transport requires a supply of energy to drive proton pumps in the cell surface membrane. Hydrogen ions are pumped out of the cells across the cell surface membrane, creating electrochemical gradients for selective ion uptake by specific transport proteins or carriers. Once inside the root cells, the ions are transported across the cortex to the endodermis via the symplast pathway.

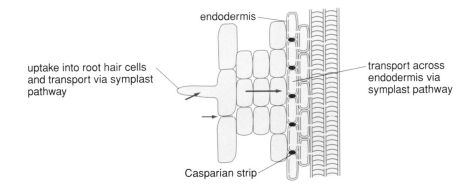

Figure 2.10 Section of root showing pathway of ions

Many of the cells of the endodermis have bands of impermeable suberin on their cell walls. These bands are referred to as **Casparian strips** and prevent the passage of water and ions into the xylem via the apoplast pathway. Water and mineral ions must pass through the cell surface membrane and cytoplasm of these cells before entering the xylem. This has prompted suggestions that the endodermis can regulate the uptake of ions by the plant. Observations of transverse sections of roots indicate the presence of certain endodermal cells, referred to as 'passage cells', that lack Casparian strips and would allow water and mineral ions to move freely into the xylem.

Figure 2.11 Casparian strips in endodermal cells and passage cells

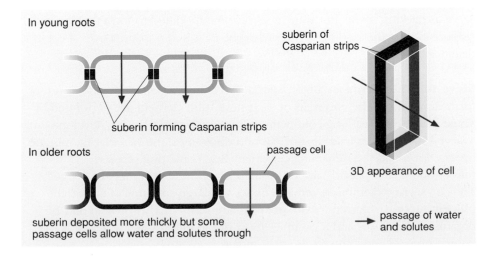

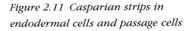

Once the ions reach the xylem, transport is by mass flow, together with water. Most ions reach the leaves, where those that are not required in synthesis may be redistributed by the phloem tissue to sites of metabolic activity such as developing buds, growing leaves, storage organs or fruits and seeds. Lateral transport from the xylem to the phloem is aided by specialised parenchyma cells called **transfer cells**. The wall of a transfer cell adjacent to a xylem vessel appears to be much folded, with large numbers of mitochondria close to the folds. The folding increases the surface area available for the uptake of ions from the xylem and the large numbers of mitochondria are able to supply the ATP necessary for this active process. Transport in the phloem is discussed in the next section of this chapter.

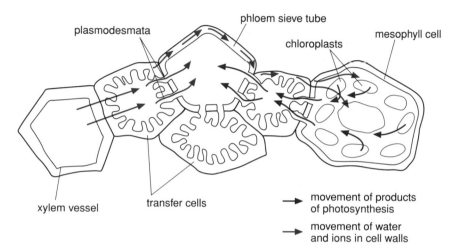

Figure 2.12 Transfer cells

Translocation of organic solutes

Organic solutes, which are the products of photosynthesis, are transported from their sites of synthesis in the leaves to other regions of the plant in the **phloem tissue**. The phloem tissue is adapted for this transport and consists of three types of cells: sieve tube elements, companion cells and phloem parenchyma. The sieve tube elements and companion cells are involved in the long-distance transport of the organic solutes. The phloem parenchyma may serve as packing tissue, but some cells become modified to form transfer cells, responsible for the loading of the sieve tube cells and transport over short distances.

Sieve tube elements are highly specialised living cells, linked end to end to form sieve tubes. The end walls of each sieve tube element are perforated by **sieve plates**, so that long conducting tubes are formed. During development, a sieve tube element loses its nucleus and ribosomes, the vacuolar membrane breaks down and the remaining cell organelles, consisting of a few mitochondria and plastids, are distributed around the periphery of the cell. The cell surface membrane remains intact and large amounts of a special phloem protein, referred to as **P-protein**, are formed. This protein may be organised into fibrils and it occupies most of the interior of the cell. It is not known precisely how the fibrils are arranged.

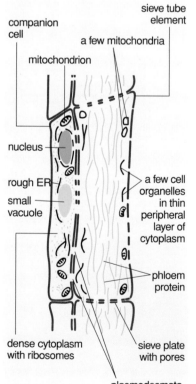

Figure 2.13 Sieve tube element and companion cell

The contents of the sieve tubes are under high hydrostatic pressure, so that when specimens of tissue are observed, it is difficult to know whether the organelles have been disturbed by the sudden release of this pressure during preparation. In some preparations, the P-protein is seen to be blocking the pores in the sieve plates, whilst in others it does not. Another material called **callose**, an insoluble polysaccharide, is often found deposited around the sieve plates. Again, it is difficult to know whether this material occurs naturally in such situations or whether it is an artefact, formed due to the procedures undergone in the preparation of the specimens. Callose is known to be formed when tissue is damaged.

Companion cells are closely associated with the sieve tube elements. Each companion cell is derived from the same parent cell as its neighbouring sieve tube element. In contrast with the sieve tube elements, companion cells retain their nuclei, ribosomes and other organelles. The cytoplasm is dense and there are large numbers of mitochondria, indicating the potential for high levels of metabolic activity. There are numerous plasmodesmata connecting the cytoplasm of the companion cell with its neighbouring sieve tube element. It is suggested that the companion cells may provide replacement P-protein, enzymes and energy for the activities of the sieve tube elements. Some companion cells appear to act as transfer cells and are involved in the movement of solutes into and out of the sieve tubes.

As previously mentioned, **phloem parenchyma cells** become modified as transfer cells. Their general function appears to be the collection and transfer of organic solutes and inorganic ions into the sieve tubes. We have already referred to these cells in connection with the redistribution of mineral ions and know that active transport is involved. Passive transport, via plasmodesmata and the symplast pathway, is also possible and known to occur in these cells.

Evidence for translocation in the phloem

Early investigations of phloem transport involved the removal of a ring of bark from the trunk of a tree to see what would happen. Such an experiment was carried out by Malpighi in 1679. He removed the bark and underlying soft tissues of the stem, leaving the xylem intact. After a few weeks, the tissue on the upper side of the ring was swollen , while that below was not. Malpighi found that the swelling only occurred if there were green leaves present on the tree and if it was kept in the light, so he deduced that substances were being made in the light and transported down the stem. At the time, this was quite a novel idea, and was some indication that a special tissue was involved, independent from that in which water transport occurred.

In the 1950s, more sophisticated techniques were developed involving the use of radioactive tracers. It was possible to supply a leaf with radioactively-labelled carbon dioxide ($^{14}CO_2$) in the light. After a period of time, stem tissue from the plant could be taken, frozen, dehydrated and cut into thin sections. If the sections were placed on photographic film, the position of any radioactively-labelled substances would show up when the film was developed. In this way, not only the tissue but also the cells involved in the transport of the organic substances could be identified.

Figure 2.14 Aphid feeding on phloem

Analysis of phloem exudates enables the contents of the phloem sap to be identified. It is possible to collect sap directly from some monocotyledonous species, such as palms, when they are cut, due to the high hydrostatic pressure forcing the sap out, but the use of aphids eliminates the possibility of contamination. Aphids are allowed to feed on a plant by inserting their stylets into the phloem tissue. Once penetration of the tissue has occurred, the aphids are anaesthetised to prevent them withdrawing their stylets and then their bodies are cut off, leaving the stylets still inserted into the phloem. Each stylet acts like a tiny pipette and sap can be collected over a number of days. This technique has its drawbacks as it is difficult to carry out and the amounts of sap collected are small. However, it can be combined with the use of radioactive tracers to provide useful information on the rate of translocation. If radioactively-labelled material is introduced, it is possible to measure the time taken for this material to be transported over a measured distance.

Using some of the techniques described above, it has been shown that phloem sap is an alkaline solution, consisting mostly of sucrose, together with organic nitrogen compounds and potassium ions. The concentration of sugars in the sap varies from 15 to 30 per cent, compared with 0.5 per cent in the leaf cells, indicating that the loading of the sieve tube elements is an active process, requiring energy. Any process or compound, such as a metabolic poison, which slows or inhibits respiration, will slow down or stop translocation in the phloem.

The mechanism of phloem transport

It has proved extremely difficult to establish the precise mechanism of phloem transport. It is known that large quantities of material are moved at rapid rates and that the conducting tissue is composed of fine tubes, but the tissue is delicate and easily damaged. It is also difficult to see how the roles of P-protein and the sieve plates can be accounted for in most of the theories put forward. The most acceptable model of phloem transport is the **pressure flow hypothesis**, based on an hypothesis put forward by Munch in 1930. He suggested that the movement of substances depended on a gradient of hydrostatic pressure. The sieve tubes in the leaves, at the **source** end of the

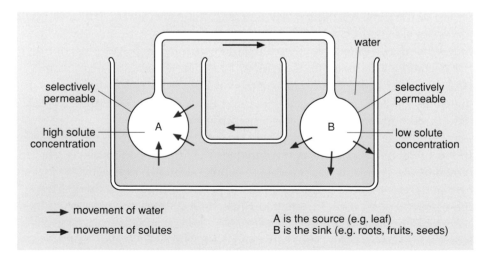

Figure 2.15 A model illustrating the pressure flow hypothesis

system, have a higher hydrostatic pressure than the sieve tubes in places such as the roots, apical meristems or seeds, known as the **sink**.

In the model (Figure 2.15), A represents the source and B the sink. The solute concentration at A will be higher than at B and water will enter A by osmosis. As water enters, a high hydrostatic pressure builds up, forcing water out of B. Mass flow of the contents of A along to B results, due to the hydrostatic pressure gradient. If this model is applied to the situation in living plants, it can be appreciated that there would be high concentrations of sugars at A due to photosynthesis in the leaves. Water enters the leaf cells by osmosis, increasing their turgor pressure. It is known that sugars will be used for respiration and synthesis in other regions of the plant, represented by B, so solutes and water will move out, resulting in a lower hydrostatic pressure at B. Mass flow occurs along the phloem from the source to the sink.

The pressure flow hypothesis predicts that a pressure gradient exists along sieve tubes and, although difficult to measure, such a pressure gradient has been demonstrated. It is not known whether the gradient would account for the rapid transport of materials in phloem tissue, but it is possible to work out a theoretical value based on the diameter of the sieve tubes and the nature of any obstacles, such as sieve plates, P-protein or callose. The hypothesis also suggests that the water and solutes move together at the same rate in the same direction. In some of the experiments carried out with radioactively-labelled sugars and water, the sugars moved at a more rapid rate, but it was suggested that as the sieve tubes were permeable to water, some moved out into the surrounding tissues.

Munch's original hypothesis was a purely physical one and did not include any reference to living tissues or the possibility of active transport. It would seem necessary to modify the original hypothesis to account for the active transport of solutes into the sieve tubes in the leaf and the unloading of solutes at the sinks, but mass flow seems to account for the movement once the solutes have reached the phloem tissue.

Transport in mammals

The circulatory system
The function of the circulatory system is the transport of nutrients and other substances, including gases, hormones and excretory products, to and from various parts of the body. The blood must therefore be kept in a state of continuous circulation, the energy for which is provided by the heart. The force of contraction of the heart propels blood to the tissues through thick-walled **arteries** and back to the heart through the thinner-walled **veins**. In the tissues, blood passes through a network of **capillaries** in which exchange of materials occurs between blood and the tissue fluid.

Mammals have a double circulatory system, which consists of the **systemic circulation** in which blood is pumped from the left side of the heart to the various tissues and organs of the body, and the **pulmonary circulation** in which blood is pumped from the right side of the heart to the pulmonary capillaries of the lungs.

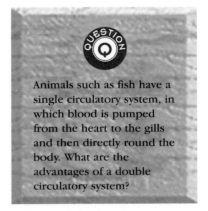

Animals such as fish have a single circulatory system, in which blood is pumped from the heart to the gills and then directly round the body. What are the advantages of a double circulatory system?

Structure and function of the heart

The human heart weighs about 300 g and is situated in the middle region of the thorax. The lower border of the heart, known as the apex, points towards the left of the thorax. The structure of the heart and major blood vessels is shown in Figure 2.16.

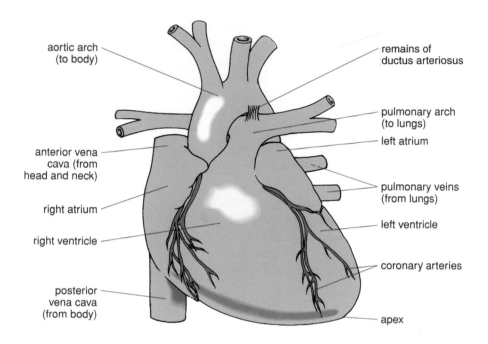

aortic arch (to body)

remains of ductus arteriosus

pulmonary arch (to lungs)

left atrium

anterior vena cava (from head and neck)

pulmonary veins (from lungs)

right atrium

left ventricle

right ventricle

coronary arteries

posterior vena cava (from body)

apex

Figure 2.16 Anterior view of the heart and major blood vessels.

The wall of the heart is made up of three distinct layers:
- an outer **epicardium**, consisting of a layer of flattened epithelial cells and supporting connective tissue
- a very thick, muscular **myocardium**, consisting of **cardiac muscle**
- an inner **endocardium**, consisting of flattened epithelial cells supported by a delicate layer of connective tissue.

Cardiac muscle consists of many branching cells, each of which may contain one or two nuclei. Cardiac muscle cells are joined by structures known as **intercalated discs**, specialised junctions between cells which both transmit the force of contraction and allow the rapid spread of electrical excitation throughout the myocardium. In histological preparations, intercalated discs appear as dark, transverse lines, as seen in Figure 2.17. Notice too that cardiac muscle has cross-striations, similar to those of skeletal muscle.

Cardiac muscle is said to be **myogenic**. This means that, unlike striated muscle, cardiac muscle is self-exciting. Cardiac muscle cells show a continuous, inherent rhythm of electrical excitation and contraction on their own, although this can be changed by nervous or hormonal influences. Cardiac muscle has a very dense capillary network which receives blood by means of the left and right **coronary arteries**. These are the first branches from the aorta and, at rest, receive about 5 per cent of the total **cardiac output**.

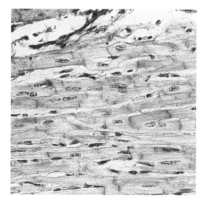

Figure 2.17 Histology of cardiac muscle, as seen using a light microscope

After passing through the capillaries, blood returns mainly via a series of cardiac veins which drain into the right atrium via a channel known as the coronary sinus. Some smaller veins from the right ventricle do not enter the coronary sinus but drain directly into the right atrium.

The interior of the heart is divided into four chambers, two upper **atria** and two lower **ventricles**. The atria receive blood from veins which return it to the heart. The atria contract and push blood into the ventricles which then contract with considerable force and pump blood into the arteries. The myocardium of the ventricles is thicker than that of the atria and the myocardium of the left ventricle is much thicker than that of the right ventricle. The left ventricle pumps blood into the aorta and around the entire body at a higher pressure than the right ventricle, which pumps blood into the pulmonary arteries and through the pulmonary capillaries.

The rhythmic sequence of events which occurs each time the heart beats is known as the **cardiac cycle**. At rest, the heart beats about 72 times per minute, so each cycle lasts about 0.83 seconds. The cardiac cycle consists of:

- **atrial systole** – contraction of the atria
- **ventricular systole** – contraction of the ventricles
- **complete cardiac diastole** – relaxation of the atria and ventricles.

The heart valves

The heart valves ensure that blood flows in one direction only and are essential for the normal function of the heart. The **atrioventricular (AV) valves** are situated between the two atria and the ventricles, at the atrioventricular orifices. The right atrioventricular valve has three flaps and is also known as the **tricuspid valve**. The left atrioventricular valve is similar in structure but has two, rather than three flaps, and is therefore called the **bicuspid**, or **mitral valve**. These valves prevent blood from flowing back into the atria when the ventricles contract and ensure that blood moves into the aorta and pulmonary arteries. The free edges of these valves are attached to papillary muscles, small projections of the inner walls of the ventricles, by chordae tendinae which prevent the valves from opening upwards. The opening of the pulmonary trunk is guarded by the **pulmonary semilunar valve** and the opening of the aorta is guarded by the **aortic semilunar valve**. When the semilunar valves close during diastole, blood is prevented from flowing back into the ventricles from the aorta and pulmonary arteries.

It is the closure of these valves which is responsible for the heart sounds. During the cardiac cycle, the atrioventricular valves close simultaneously at the start of ventricular systole. This produces the first heart sound, followed shortly afterwards by the second sound, produced by the closure of the semilunar valves indicating the start of diastole. The first and second heart sounds are frequently described as 'lubb' and 'dup' respectively and may be heard using a stethoscope.

The conducting system of the heart

The rhythmic sequence of events during the cardiac cycle is coordinated by tissues within the heart itself. These tissues consist of modified cardiac muscle

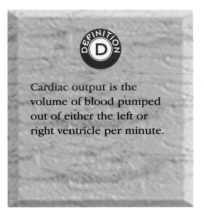

Definition D

Cardiac output is the volume of blood pumped out of either the left or right ventricle per minute.

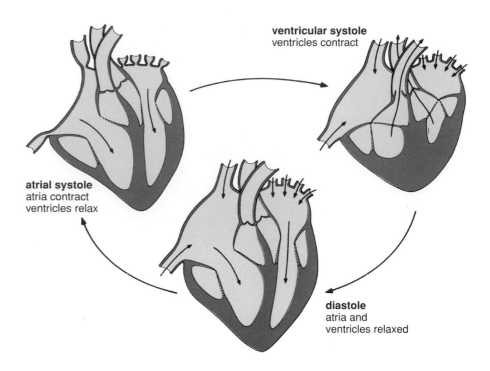

Figure 2.18 Chambers and valves of the heart showing the action of the heart chambers during atrial systole and ventricular systole

cells which, in humans, are not easy to distinguish from other cardiac muscle cells. The conducting system comprises:

- the sinuatrial, or sinoatrial, (SA) node
- the atrioventricular (AV) node
- the bundle of His and its branches.

The sinuatrial node (SA node) consists of a small group of specialised cells situated in the wall of the right atrium, near the opening of the superior vena cava. The SA node is often referred to as the **pacemaker** as it initiates the heart beat by sending out a wave of electrical excitation which spreads over the right and left atria. This stimulates the myocardium to contract. The atrioventricular node (AV node) is situated in the wall of the right atrium, near the opening of the coronary sinus. The wave of excitation reaches the AV node and is conducted, via the bundle of His and branches, to the ventricular myocardium. The bundle of His and its branches consist of Purkinje (or Purkyne) tissue – modified cardiac muscle. This arrangement of the conducting tissues ensures that there is a delay between contraction of the atria and contraction of the ventricles and that the electrical excitation reaches most of the ventricular cells simultaneously, which ensures a single, coordinated contraction. The conducting system of the heart is illustrated in Figure 2.19.

The electrical impulses which accompany contraction of the heart are conducted through body fluids and can be recorded by placing electrodes on the surface of the skin, either on the chest wall, or on the wrists and ankles. The pattern of electrical activity can then be displayed on an oscilloscope screen, or printed out onto paper. This recording is known as an

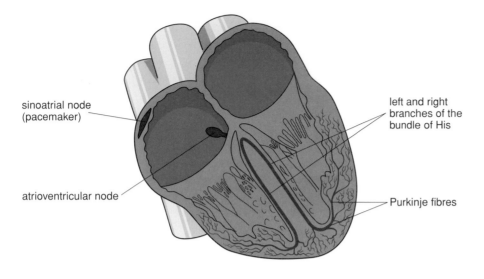

Figure 2.19 *The conducting system of the human heart*

electrocardiogram, or **ECG**, and shows changes in voltage against time. A normal ECG shows five waves, which are conventionally referred to as the P wave, the QRS complex and the T wave (Figure 2.20)

The P wave is caused by electrical excitation of the atria, the QRS complex indicates excitation of the ventricles and the T wave is due to recovery (repolarisation) of the ventricles. The ECG has considerable clinical importance as it indicates abnormalities in the pattern of excitation of the heart. Part of an ECG from a healthy patient is shown in Figure 2.20.

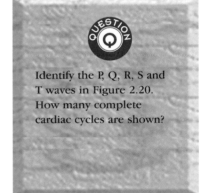

Identify the P, Q, R, S and T waves in Figure 2.20. How many complete cardiac cycles are shown?

Pressure changes in the heart

Figure 2.21 shows the pressure changes in the heart during a cardiac cycle, starting with the beginning of atrial systole at time 0. Notice that although the pressure in the ventricles drops to zero during diastole, the pressure within the aorta and pulmonary artery remains relatively high. This pressure is

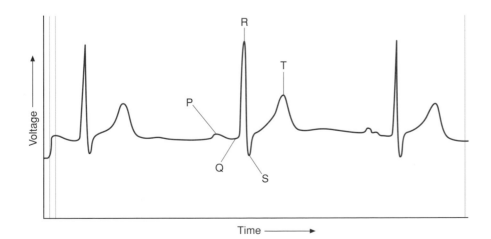

Figure 2.20 *Part of an ECG recording*

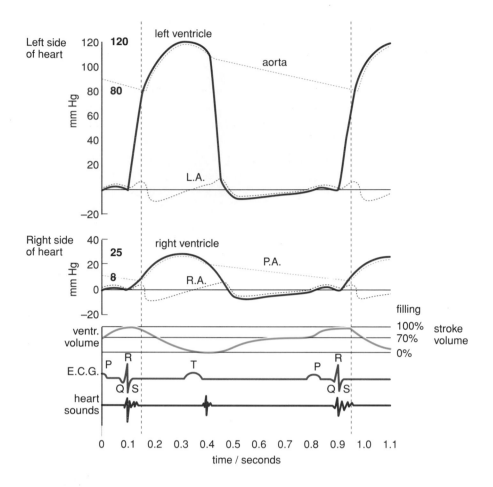

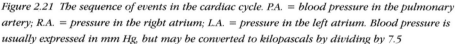

Figure 2.21 The sequence of events in the cardiac cycle. P.A. = blood pressure in the pulmonary artery; R.A. = pressure in the right atrium; L.A. = pressure in the left atrium. Blood pressure is usually expressed in mm Hg, but may be converted to kilopascals by dividing by 7.5

maintained by the closure of the semilunar valves and by the elastic recoil of the arterial walls.

Nervous and hormonal control of the rate of heart beat

The heart is supplied by nerves of the autonomic nervous system. Sympathetic and parasympathetic (vagus nerve) fibres combine to form cardiac plexuses, situated near the aortic arch. From here, nerve fibres enter the heart and most end in the SA node, but some end in the AV node and the atrial myocardium. Although the SA node normally initiates the heart beat, the rate can be changed by a number of factors, including the ratio of impulses in the sympathetic and parasympathetic nerves to the SA node. Increased sympathetic activity will increase the heart rate, whereas increased parasympathetic activity will decrease heart rate.

Reflexes involving factors such as exercise, hormones, blood temperature and pain can also affect heart rate. In exercise, for example, the heart rate normally increases. The precise mechanism for this is not known, but it involves impulses from the cerebrum, through the hypothalamus to the cardiac centre in the medulla oblongata. Adrenaline, released from the adrenal medulla, acts directly on the heart and increases both the heart rate and the cardiac output.

Coronary heart disease, artificial pacemakers and heart transplants

Heart disease is a major cause of death in the Western world and accounts for over 160 000 deaths each year in the United Kingdom. The main causes are coronary artery **atherosclerosis** and **ischaemic heart disease**. Atherosclerosis is a condition in which lipids and other substances, including collagen-like fibres, build up on the inside wall of blood vessels. The consequences of this are:

- narrowing of the lumen of the artery, which obstructs blood flow
- formation of a blood clot (thrombosis) which may block the vessel
- aneurysm due to weakening of the vessel wall due to loss of muscle and elastic fibres.

Impairment of blood flow in any part of a coronary artery means that blood cannot reach the heart muscle cells which it normally supplies. If these cells are deprived of oxygen, they may soon die, the area of tissue involved being described as an infarct. Disturbance of blood supply may not always be sufficient to cause tissue death, but may instead cause temporary damage to the tissue. This situation is known as ischacmia which may, though not always, lead to infarction. **Myocardial infarction** (heart attack) is a common cause of death during middle and late adulthood. There are a number of risk factors associated with the development of atherosclerosis and ischaemic heart disease, including:

- age and sex – an increasing incidence occurs with age and is higher in males up to the age of 75
- cigarette smoking – especially over 20 cigarettes per day and in young people
- high plasma lipoprotein levels, particularly high density types
- genetic – some families have an increased risk which is independent of other factors
- diabetes mellitus.

On occasions, myocardial infarction results in damage to the conducting system of the heart. As a result, the atria may continue to beat normally but the ventricles, which no longer receive impulses via the bundles of His, start to contract but much more slowly than is required to maintain adequate cardiac output. Patients may become very short of breath, or suffer from dizziness or blackouts. This condition can be treated by the insertion of an **artificial pacemaker**, a device which delivers an electrical stimulus to the heart muscle. There are several different types of artificial pacemakers, including permanent pacemakers, which are inserted into the patient's chest and connected to the apex of the heart via a pacing wire. The pacemaker is powered by lithium batteries and generates an electrical stimulus which ensures that the ventricles contract at a steady rate of 60 to 70 beats per minute. Some advanced types of pacemakers, known as rate-responsive pacemakers, can alter the rate of stimulation to match physiological demand. For example, the rate will increase during physical exercise.

Heart transplants are surgical procedures in which healthy hearts are removed from donors and used to replace the hearts of patients who are

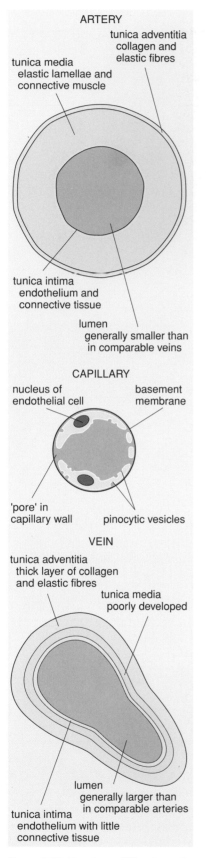

Figure 2.22 Structure of blood vessels (not to same scale)

otherwise likely to die because of heart disease. A healthy heart is removed from a donor after brain stem death and packed in a sterile plastic bag surrounded by crushed ice. A heart may be stored in this way, prior to transplantation, and will remain viable for up to four hours.

Arteries, capillaries and veins

Arteries are blood vessels which transport blood away from the heart. Although arteries vary in diameter, they all have a similar structure, consisting of three layers of tissue:

- an inner tunica intima, consisting of flattened epithelial cells (endothelium) and their supporting connective tissue
- a middle tunica media, containing smooth muscle cells and elastic fibres
- an outer tunica adventitia consisting of connective tissue.

Arterioles are defined as vessels of the arterial system with a diameter of less than 0.3 mm. Their tunica media consists almost entirely of smooth muscle cells. Arterioles divide repeatedly and become progressively smaller in diameter, eventually leading into **capillaries**. The wall of a capillary consists of a single layer of flattened epithelial cells, which allow efficient exchange of materials between blood and the surrounding tissue fluid. The diameter of capillaries varies, but is typically about 7 μm, approximately the same as that of a red blood cell. Capillary networks drain into venules, then **veins**, which return blood to the heart. The wall of a vein has the same three layers as the wall of an artery, but the wall is very much thinner in relation to the diameter of the lumen. Some veins contain valves: delicate projections of the tunica intima. These valves are present mainly in the veins of the limbs and prevent backflow of blood. The structures of an artery, capillary and vein are shown in Figure 2.22.

Blood pressure

The term **blood pressure** usually refers to the pressure within the aorta and main arteries. The pressure is not constant, but varies between a minimum (or diastolic) value and a maximum (or systolic) value. Blood pressure is usually measured in mm Hg, although this is not an SI unit. Typical blood pressures for an adult at rest are about 120 mm Hg (systolic) and about 80 mm Hg (diastolic), usually written as 120/80 mm Hg. However, it must be noted that these figures will vary according to the time of day (there is a circadian rhythm of changes in blood pressure), posture, sex and age of the person.

Blood pressure depends on a number of factors including:
- cardiac output
- blood volume
- peripheral resistance (resistance to blood flow mainly due to the diameter of arterioles)
- elasticity of artery walls
- volume of blood returning to the heart.

As an example, cardiac output depends on the volume of blood pumped out of the ventricles with each beat, and the heart rate. Any factor which makes the heart beat faster, or makes it beat more strongly and increases the stroke volume, will increase cardiac output and will therefore tend to increase blood pressure. High blood pressure, or **hypertension**, occurs when the diastolic pressure exceeds 95 mm Hg and the systolic pressure exceeds 160 mm Hg (World Health Organisation classification). Many risk factors have been identified in the development of hypertension and include:

- genetic factors
- sex – men experience higher rates of hypertension at an earlier age than women
- age
- high stress levels
- obesity
- smoking.

There are numerous complications of untreated hypertension, including heart failure, kidney failure, atherosclerosis and stroke.

Blood and body fluids

Blood is a tissue consisting of a variety of cells suspended in a fluid medium known as **plasma**. Blood functions mainly as a transport medium throughout the body for respiratory gases (oxygen and carbon dioxide), nutrients, hormones, metabolic waste products and cells. Plasma consists of 90 per cent water and 10 per cent solutes, including proteins, nutrients, excretory products, dissolved gases, hormones, enzymes and other substances. Plasma proteins are of three types: albumins, globulins and fibrinogen. Albumins and fibrinogen are important in the blood-clotting mechanism; globulins are essential parts of the immune system.

There are three varieties of cells present in blood:

- erythrocytes, or red blood cells
- leucocytes, or white blood cells
- thrombocytes, or platelets.

All blood cells develop from multipotential stem cells, which are present in the bone marrow. Stem cells divide to replicate themselves and to give rise to separate cell types, each of which divides and develops to form one of the main blood cell types. White blood cells are subdivided into two main groups: **granulocytes** and **agranulocytes**. Granulocytes have prominent granules in their cytoplasm and a multilobed nucleus. There are three types of granulocytes: **neutrophils**, **eosinophils** and **basophils**. Agranulocytes, which are either **monocytes** or **lymphocytes**, have nongranular cytoplasm and their nuclei are not lobed, although the nucleus of a monocyte may be strongly indented. The structures and functions of blood cells are summarised in Table 2.1.

Transport of oxygen and carbon dioxide

Oxygen combines with haemoglobin, present in red blood cells, to form oxyhaemoglobin. Each gram of haemoglobin can combine with 1.34 cm^3 of oxygen, so the total amount of oxygen which can be carried in the blood depends mainly on the amount of haemoglobin present. The relationship between the partial pressure of oxygen and the quantity of oxygen combined

TRANSPORT SYSTEMS

Table 2.1 *Cell types present in the blood of humans*

Cell type	Size / μm	Number per cm^3	Function
erythrocyte	6 to 8	4 to 6 million	transport of respiratory gases
neutrophil	10 to 12	2800 to 5250	phagocytosis of pathogenic microorganisms
eosinophil	10 to 12	70 to 420	secrete 'major basic protein' which is involved in defence against certain parasitic worms
basophil	9 to 10	0 to 70	secrete heparin and histamine
lymphocyte	7 to 8	1400 to 3150	secrete antibodies
monocyte	14 to 17	140 to 700	migrate out of blood to form macrophages: phagocytic cells which engulf bacteria and cell debris
platelets	2 to 3	150 000 to 400 000	release thromboplastin, which is important in blood clotting

with haemoglobin is an S-shaped curve, referred to as the **oxygen dissociation curve**.

The exact position of this curve depends on a number of factors, including the partial pressure of carbon dioxide, temperature and pH. For example, if the partial pressure of carbon dioxide increases, the curve moves to the right (known as the Bohr effect). This decreases the affinity of haemoglobin for oxygen, which will therefore be released more readily.

Fetal haemoglobin (haemoglobin F), has a higher affinity for oxygen than adult haemoglobin at any given partial pressure of oxygen. This means that fetal haemoglobin will receive oxygen from the maternal haemoglobin at the same partial pressure of oxygen. Myoglobin is a pigment found in muscles, particularly the leg muscles and hearts of large mammals. Like haemoglobin, myoglobin can combine reversibly with oxygen, but myoglobin takes up oxygen much more readily than does haemoglobin. When blood reaches muscle tissue, oxygen is transferred from oxyhaemoglobin to myoglobin, which acts as a temporary oxygen store in the muscles.

Carbon dioxide, produced in respiration, diffuses from body tissues into the blood, where most of it is taken up by red blood cells. In the red blood cells, carbon dioxide combines with water and forms hydrogencarbonate ions (HCO_3^-):

$$CO_2 + H_2O \rightarrow H_2CO_3 \rightarrow H^+ + HCO_3^-$$

The hydrogencarbonate then diffuses into the plasma in exchange for chloride ions. The majority of carbon dioxide is transported in the form of hydrogencarbonate. Carbon dioxide also reacts with haemoglobin and other proteins to form carbamino compounds, and a relatively small percentage of carbon dioxide is transported in simple solution.

Carbon monoxide

Carbon monoxide (CO), a pollutant gas present in car exhaust fumes and cigarette smoke, can combine with haemoglobin to form carboxyhaemoglobin. Carbon monoxide has about 250 times as great an affinity for haemoglobin than has oxygen and combines with the haem group, preventing oxygen from doing so. Death occurs in humans who are exposed to concentrations of carbon monoxide of around 1000 p.p.m. (parts per million), which corresponds to a blood carboxyhaemoglobin concentration of 60 per cent. Adverse effects, including dizziness, headaches and mental confusion are experienced at concentrations considerably lower than this. The actual concentration of carboxyhaemoglobin in the blood of cigarette smokers varies between 1.2 and 9 per cent. Because carbon monoxide blocks the transport of oxygen, it has been suggested that carbon monoxide is a contributing factor in heart disease.

Interchange of materials between capillaries and tissue fluid

The walls of capillaries consist of a single layer of flattened epithelial cells, which act as a selectively permeable membrane, allowing water and solutes of low molecular mass to pass through. Proteins remain in the capillaries. Tissue

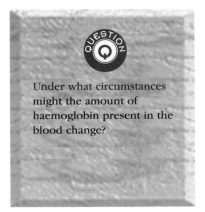

Under what circumstances might the amount of haemoglobin present in the blood change?

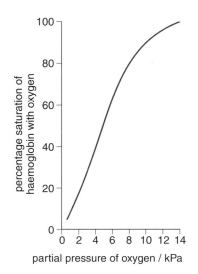

Figure 2.23 The oxygen dissociation curve

TRANSPORT SYSTEMS

Use of this fact can be made to find the water potential of a plant tissue, such as potato, by immersing pieces in a range of solutions (referred to as graded osmotica) and determining the changes in mass of the tissue.

Materials

- Large potato
- Cork borer (1 cm diameter)
- Graded sucrose solutions (0.2 mol dm^{-3}, 0.4 mol dm^{-3}, 0.6 mol dm^{-3} and 0.8 mol dm^{-3})
- Sharp knife
- Petri dishes
- Filter paper
- Ruler
- Electronic balance

Method

1 Set up five Petri dishes containing the above sucrose solutions. A zero ψ treatment should also be included using tap water, rather than distilled water. Label each dish on its base.
2 Using the cork borer, cut cores of potato tissue then slice into discs 1 mm thick. Place six discs on each of five pieces of filter paper.
3 Gently blot and weigh each group of discs. Record the mass of each group then place into each of the labelled dishes.
4 After *at least 30 minutes*, remove the discs, blot carefully and reweigh.

Results and discussion

1 Record all your results in a table and calculate the percentage change in mass (change in mass multiplied by 100, divided by the original mass) for each group of discs.
2 Using the information in Table 2.5, plot a graph of the percentage change in mass (vertical axis) against the solute potential of the bathing solution (horizontal axis).
3 Where this curve cuts the horizontal axis, $\psi_{tissue} = \psi_{solution}$.
4 Record the ψ_{tissue} from your graph.
5 If the curve has a kink below the horizontal axis, the kink will be approximately in the region of ψ_s for the cell sap. This is because once incipient plasmolysis has been reached, very little further changes in mass occur.
6 What are the sources of error in this experiment?

Table 2.5 *Solute potentials of sucrose solutions*

Concentration of sucrose solution / mol dm^{-3}	Solute potential ($\psi_{solution}$) / kPa
0.2	-540
0.4	-1130
0.6	-1800
0.8	-2580

Further work

1 If a suitable balance is not available, satisfactory results can be obtained by measuring changes in the dimensions of a strip of tissue. Strips should be no less than 5 cm in length and about 0.5 cm thick.

2 If sufficient time is available, the groups of discs should be removed from their bathing solutions, blotted carefully, weighed and replaced in their bathing solutions. Readings should be taken every 30 minutes for 2.5 hours and changes in mass of each group can be plotted against time until equilibrium is reached.

3 Investigate tissue water potentials using other plant materials, such as other storage roots and tubers, leaf discs or hypocotyl sections of seedlings.

Determination of the solute potential of cell sap

Introduction

Incipient plasmolysis is the point at which the plant cell contents (known as the protoplast) are *just* about to lose contact with the cell wall as water is lost from the cell by osmosis. At the point of incipient plasmolysis, the pressure potential (ψ_p) is zero therefore, from the general equation

$$\psi_{cell} = \psi_s$$

If plant cells are immersed in a graded osmotica then examined microscopically, it is likely that signs of plasmolysis will be seen in cells immersed in one of these solutions. Cells in other solutions will either be turgid or fully plasmolysed.

In practice, the point of incipient plasmolysis is taken to be when half the number of cells observed show signs of plasmolysis.

Materials

- Rhubarb petioles (rhubarb epidermis is preferable to onion epidermis as the cytoplasm in rhubarb is strongly pigmented and plasmolysis is therefore easier to see)
- Graded sucrose solutions, as in previous experiment
- Scissors
- Watch glasses or other suitable containers
- Pipettes
- Microscope slides and coverslips
- Mounted needles
- Microscope

Method

1 Label small dishes appropriately and add sucrose solutions separately to each. One dish should contain tap water as a zero ψ control.

2 Carefully peel the pigmented epidermis from a rhubarb petiole and, using scissors, cut into squares with sides approximately 5 mm.

3 Immediately place one square of tissue into each of the osmotica.

4 Leave the tissue in these solutions for 10 minutes.

5 After 10 minutes, remove each strip one at a time using a mounted needle and mount on a microscope slide in a drop of the same solution in which it had been immersed.

6 Apply a coverslip and examine using a microscope, first with low power, then high.

7 Count all the cells which are visible within the field of view, then count all the cells which show signs of plasmolysis. Include all cells in which it is possible to see separation of the cell contents from the cell wall, no matter how slight this may be. If you are unsure of the appearance of plasmolysed cells, look at your preparation from 0.8 mol dm^{-3} sucrose solution first.

8 For each preparation, count three separate fields of view.

9 Make a labelled drawing to show the appearance of a plasmolysed cell.

Results and discussion

1 Calculate the mean percentage of cells which show signs of plasmolysis in each of the osmotica. Tabulate your results clearly.

2 Using the information in Table 2.5, plot a graph of the mean percentage of cells plasmolysed (vertical axis) against the solute potential of the bathing solution (horizontal axis).

3 From your graph, read off the solute potential of the sucrose solution which corresponds to 50 per cent plasmolysis.

4 Explain why this solution may be regarded as having the same solute potential as the cell sap.

Preparation of an epidermal peel and observation of stomata

Introduction

The use of *Commelina communis* is recommended for the preparation of epidermal peels, as it is possible to remove the lower epidermis relatively easily, with little or no damage to the stomata. As an alternative, leaves of *Vicia faba* (broad bean) may be used. *C. communis* can be easily grown from seed, which should be sown about six weeks before the leaves are required. If sown individually in 100 mm pots, the seeds will germinate after about one week at 20 to 25 °C, and after another four weeks the plants should have up to 10 mature leaves. It is important to keep the compost well watered.

An initial supply of *C. communis* seed can be obtained by sending a stamped, self-addressed envelope to: Dr J. Weyers, Department of Biological Sciences, University of Dundee, Dundee DD1 4HN, Scotland.

Materials

- *Commelina communis* plants, or a suitable alternative
- Scalpel or single-edged razor blade
- Microscope slides and coverslips
- Microscope
- Stage micrometer

Method

1 Carefully tear a detached leaf, using a slight twisting action, to remove the lower epidermis.

2 Cut the epidermis into pieces about 5 mm × 5 mm.

3 Mount each piece separately in a drop of water on a microscope slide and apply a coverslip.

4 Use a stage micrometer to measure the diameter of the field of view, at high magnification (40 × objective).

5 Observe the epidermal strip and, at high magnification, count the number of stomata per field of view. Repeat several times and find the mean number. Compare with the photograph in Figure 2.6.

Results and discussion

1 Make a careful, labelled diagram to show the structure of the stomatal complex, including the guard cells, subsidiary cells and epidermal cells. The subsidiary and epidermal cells of *C. communis* may contain calcium oxalate crystals (raphides), the function of which is not known.

2 Calculate the area of the field of view, and determine the number of stomata per mm^2. This is known as the **stomatal frequency**.

3 Find the surface area of one typical leaf, for example by placing the leaf on graph paper and carefully drawing around it. How many stomata are there on the lower surface of the leaf?

Further work

1 Observe the arrangements of stomata and compare the stomatal frequencies on the upper and lower epidermis of leaves from different species.

2 Permanent preparations of leaf epidermis can be made using clear nail varnish replicas. This method is suitable for species from which it is difficult to remove the epidermis. A small area (about 1 cm^2) of the epidermis should be painted *thinly* with clear nail varnish, which is then allowed to dry completely. The nail varnish replica can be easily transferred to a microscope slide using a piece of transparent adhesive tape.

3 Positive replicas of leaf epidermis can be made using a dental silicone impression material, such as Provil®. The base and catalyst are mixed together in approximately equal proportions, then spread onto a leaf. The material sets rapidly and, after removing, can be used to prepare positive impressions using clear nail varnish. This method provides striking results.

3 Chemical coordination

Both plants and animals require some form of internal coordination so that growth and development can occur successfully and so that appropriate responses can be made to environmental stimuli. There are two ways in which this coordination may occur:

- by means of chemical substances, referred to as hormones in animals and growth substances in plants
- by the nervous system, found only in animals.

This chapter looks at the principles of chemical coordination before considering a range of plant growth substances and some examples of hormonal control in mammals.

The chemicals which control and coordinate events in both plants and animals are only required in small quantities, but that is where the major similarities end. They are different classes of chemicals, the plant compounds tending to be more complex than the animal. Mammalian hormones are produced by endocrine glands, secreted into the blood and transported to their target organs, which may be some distance away from their site of synthesis. Plant growth substances do not necessarily need to be transported away from their site of synthesis and nearly always affect some aspect of growth.

Plant growth substances

Plant growth substances are organic chemical substances which coordinate and regulate a range of activities within a plant, and are concerned mainly with control of growth and development. They are produced in one part of a plant and are usually translocated to another part where they cause a physiological response. Naturally occurring (endogenous) plant growth substances act at very low concentrations and their actions may promote or inhibit certain processes of growth and development. Artificial chemical substances have been synthesised and some of these have important commercial applications because of their effects on plants. Such chemicals are often described as **plant regulators**. The term **plant growth substance** is preferred to **plant hormone**.

Generally, five groups of plant growth substances are recognised: **auxins**, **gibberellins**, **cytokinins**, **abscisic acid** and **ethene**. Auxins, gibberellins and cytokinins can be considered as growth **promotors** (stimulators), and are involved in processes such as cell division, cell elongation, differentiation of cells and initiation of organs. Abscisic acid and ethene are often associated with processes occurring late in plant development and act mainly as growth **inhibitors** or as antagonists to the growth stimulators. The chemical structures of substances in each of the groups illustrate their diverse nature. In addition to their individual effects, the substances can interact with each other, either **synergistically** (whereby the effects are enhanced by two or more growth substances acting together) or **antagonistically** (whereby the effects counteract each other).

We can see parallels with animal hormones. As you go through this section, look for ways that plant growth substances are similar to animal hormones and ways in which plant growth substances differ from animal hormones.

54

Experimental work with auxins and other plant growth substances, often relies on exogenous (external) application of the substance, say on excised sections of stems or coleoptiles. Care must be taken in the interpretation of these experiments in that they provide only indirect evidence for the activity of the growth substance within the living material. This is partly because of the very low concentrations at which growth substances occur and also a reflection of the complex interactions of one plant growth substance with others.

Experimental evidence for plant growth substances

The discovery of plant growth substances began with experiments carried out over 100 years ago, towards the end of the 19th century. Early workers searched for some understanding of plant growth involved in tropisms. Later experiments led to the concept that there are **chemical messengers** which control and coordinate growth and development within the plant and also its responses.

Much of the experimental work has been carried out using the first shoots of seeds of the grass family, known as **coleoptiles**. The coleoptile is the sheath covering the plumule or first shoot of the germinating embryo. Inside the coleoptile lie the **apical meristem** and **leaf primordia**. These parts contain actively dividing cells, and these are the cells which differentiate to become new structures in the shoot. The leaf primordia contain the cells which develop into leaves. Coleoptiles are useful for experimental work because they are very sensitive to light and, in the dark, they grow at first like a stem.

Classic experiments carried out by Darwin (1880), Boysen Jensen (1913), Paal (1919) and Went (1926) are still relevant today, both as a means for understanding plant growth substances and as a basis for further experimentation. Went was the first to use the term **auxin** for the growth promoting chemical substance from excised coleoptile tips that could diffuse into agar blocks. This discovery has been very useful for further experimentation (see Chapter 5).

Auxins

The term auxin now refers to a group of plant growth substances, involved generally with elongation growth in coleoptiles and many stems. Auxins also affect other processes such as initiation of roots, dormancy in lateral buds and fruit development. There are a number of naturally occurring auxins, of which **indole-3-acetic acid** (**IAA**) is the most important. Some synthetic auxins have important applications on a commercial scale in horticulture and agriculture.

IAA is synthesised in regions of active cell division and enlargement, notably the apical meristems (at the tip) of shoots and in young leaves. Transport of IAA away from the apex to older organs is in one direction (polar) and is by an active process which requires energy, with the auxin passing from cell to cell. Transport from sites of synthesis in leaves appears to be nonpolar, and occurs in the phloem. This is primarily a passive process, allowing the auxin to move up or down the plant at speeds considerably faster than that achieved by the polar transport.

Auxins promote growth by increasing the plasticity of the cell wall. As the cell wall softens, the cell becomes less turgid and so takes up more water, resulting in expansion of the cell. In the apical growing regions, because of the orientation of cellulose microfibrils in the cell wall, cell expansion tends to be in a longitudinal direction leading to elongation. There is evidence to suggest that the softening of the cell wall is linked to an **acidification** process in which hydrogen ions (H^+) are pumped, by an active process, out of the cell. The resulting decrease in pH activates enzymes which promote break down of bonds within the cell wall structure, leading to the loosening of the cell wall. The process of wall expansion is irreversible and auxin may also promote the synthesis of new wall material, ensuring continued growth. It is likely that, in addition to this rapid short-term effect on cell elongation, auxin also exerts an effect through the activation or repression of specific genes involved in growth responses.

The experiments described in Chapter 5 show how auxins are linked with plant responses, known as **tropisms**. Shoots are positively **phototropic** and the curvature towards light is the result of increased elongation of cells in the growing region on the shaded side. This is brought about by a re-distribution of auxin, laterally across the shoot (Figure 5.12). Similarly, in shoots, the upward curvature of horizontal shoots as a negatively **geotropic** response is consistent with there being an accumulation of auxin on the lower side, though the mechanism for this redistribution is not clearly understood. In roots, the positive geotropic response is thought to be linked to **statoliths**, (see Chapter 5, pages 98 – 99). The positioning of the statoliths within the cell is believed to enable detection of the direction of gravity and to be responsible for the redistribution of auxin at the root tip, giving an accumulation on the lower side. It is probable that calcium ions are involved. However, since roots are positively geotropic, the downward curvature of horizontal roots must be the result of a net increase in growth on the upper side of the root. This conflicts with the behaviour of auxins in shoots. The explanation may lie in the concentration being below that required for growth in the root cells, or that other plant growth substances (such as abscisic acid) are involved which have an inhibitory effect on growth on the lower surface.

Other activities of auxins are summarised below together with some examples of applications in horticulture and agriculture.

- **apical dominance** – auxin in the apical bud has an inhibitory effect on the growth of lateral (axillary) buds. If the apical bud is removed, lateral buds are likely to grow, but if auxin (say in an agar block or mixed with lanolin) is applied to the cut tip of the shoot, lateral bud growth is again inhibited. Removal of this apical dominance is an important part of the practice of pruning and may, for example, be used to stimulate bushy growth or development of fruit buds.
- **formation of lateral roots** – growth of the primary root is *inhibited* by high auxin concentrations, but auxin *stimulates* initiation of lateral roots (above the root hair zone) and of adventitious roots, particularly around wounds in roots or shoots. In horticulture, 'hormone rooting powder' is widely used to stimulate growth of adventitious roots when taking cuttings. Two synthetic auxins used in hormone rooting powder are NAA (naphthaleneacetic acid) and IBA (indole butyric acid).

- **abscission of leaves and fruit** – IAA delays early stages of leaf abscission but promotes later stages, probably through its stimulation of ethene production (page 61). It can be used to delay abscission of fruits or 'fruit drop', ensuring the fruit stays on the tree until harvest.
- **fruit development** – auxin is produced in pollen and in the developing seed and probably acts as the stimulus for development of the fruit after fertilisation. Treatment of unpollinated flowers with auxin may result in the development of seedless fruits.
- **synthetic auxins as weedkillers** – synthetic compounds, such as 2,4-D (2,4-dichlorophenoxyacetic acid) are used as selective weedkillers (herbicides). Their use depends on the way plants respond to different concentrations of auxins. Dicotyledons (such as thistles and dandelions) are very sensitive to 2,4-D and show abnormal growth, resulting in distortion of the internodes and rooting system, resulting in death of the plant. Monocotyledons (such as grasses and cereal crops) are unaffected, so such compounds can be used selectively to remove dicotyledonous weeds from a lawn or a field with a cereal crop.

Figure 3.1 (a) Pruning of fruit trees – removal of apical bud on these side shoots encourages development of fruit buds. In this young apple tree, summer pruning is used as a means of restricting vigorous growth and to help control the shape of the tree (b) Auxins can be used to delay abscission of fruit, ensuring fruit stays on the tree until harvest

Gibberellins

The term **gibberellin** is applied to a group of substances of similar chemical structure, some of which show biological activity. The first evidence of the existence of these plant growth substances came in the 1930s, when some Japanese scientists isolated the substance now known as gibberellic acid (GA_3) from the fungus *Gibberella fujikuroi*. It was well known that rice plants infected with this fungus grew very tall, but did not produce seeds, hence the local name of 'foolish seedling' disease. In the 1950s, the nature of gibberellins and their effects began to be known and studied more widely.

Gibberellins have now been extracted from higher plants, with the highest levels occurring in immature seeds though they have been detected in other parts of plants. Because of the low concentrations at which they occur it is difficult to be sure of their natural or **endogenous** role in regulation of plant growth. However, a number of effects are now well established for exogenously applied gibberellins and some of these are summarised below. Although there are several known gibberellins, most of the effects to be described can be brought about by the application of gibberellic acid (GA_3).

*Figure 3.2 Chinese cabbage (*Brassica rapa*) as we know it for a vegetable (left). This is the rosette form which develops during short day length. Longer day length triggers bolting and development of a flower stalk bearing flowers (right). Gibberellins can be used to induce bolting of long-day plants when the days are short*

- **stem elongation in dwarf plants** – plants that are genetically dwarf forms, when treated with gibberellic acid, show elongation of their stems to become comparable with normal or tall forms. This has been demonstrated in dwarf peas (*Pisum sativum*) and dwarf maize (*Zea mays*). Gibberellic acid has no effect on genetically normal or tall forms. Gibberellins are used in the sugarcane industry to stimulate the growth of the internodes during the winter season thus increasing the yield.
- **bolting in long-day plants** – some plants show photoperiodism with respect to their flowering, which occurs as a response to daylength. **Long-day plants** remain in a rosette form during short days and but require long days to grow a long flower stalk (bolt). This effect can be overcome by applying gibberellic acid and long-day plants made to bolt during short days. Similarly, some long-day plants have, in addition, a requirement for a cold period before flowering, and this can also be overcome by the application of gibberellic acid.
- **fruit development** – gibberellic acid can be used to promote fruit development and growth. This application is used commercially to increase the size of seedless grapes. The size and shape of the bunch is also improved because growth of the fruit stalk is stimulated. In citrus fruits, gibberellins are used to delay senescence allowing the fruits to stay longer on the tree and thus extend the market period.
- **seed germination** – some seeds have a requirement for light or cold to break dormancy and allow germination. Gibberellic acid can be used to induce germination and thus overcome these requirements.
- **enzyme production during germination of seeds** – food stored as starch is mobilised or broken down during germination by the action of hydrolytic enzymes (α– and β–amylase) (see Figure 6.14, page 127). These

two enzymes break different linkages in the starch molecule to produce maltose, which can be further broken down to glucose by the action of maltase. In barley and other grains ('seeds') in the grass family, there is evidence that endogenous gibberellins from the embryo stimulate the aleurone layer to release α–amylase. This has important application in the brewing industry which utilises germinating barley grains as a source of malt for making beer. After steeping in water, the grains are sprayed with gibberellic acid which stimulates production of enzymes: first those which break down the cell walls, then release of α–amylase, so increasing the yield of malt before fermentation by yeasts.

- **gibberellin synthesis inhibitors** – these can be used to counteract the effects described for gibberellins and prevent growth. In commercial situations they are used to keep a compact shape for certain plants, such as chrysanthemums and poinsettias, or to minimise growth of shrub plants along the roadside so that they require less frequent trimming.

Cytokinins

As the name suggests, **cytokinins** are linked to cell division (**cytokinesis**). The discovery of this group of plant growth substances came from attempts to find ways of growing cells in culture, outside the plant, similar to growing cultures of microorganisms. In plants, cells grow and differentiate, but once they have assumed their function, mature cells generally do not divide or show further changes, unless stimulated to do so. One example of renewed activity of plant cells is seen in the response to wounding.

Around the beginning of the 20th century, the German scientist Haberlandt believed that individual plant cells had the potential to develop into any type of specialised plant tissue. However, it was not until the 1950s that success was achieved in growing isolated cells in culture media. From these **tissue cultures**, whole plants were produced. A typical culture medium contains a source of energy (e.g. sucrose), a range of inorganic ions and other organic nutrients, such as amino acids and some vitamins. In the early stages, the cells being cultured are carrying out heterotrophic nutrition. A key to the success in the culturing of cells was the addition of growth regulating substances, particularly auxin and cytokinin.

Naturally occurring cytokinins have now been extracted from a wide range of living plant tissue. The first to be identified was **zeatin**, found in the immature endosperm of maize (*Zea mays*). Zeatin in the liquid endosperm of coconut ('coconut milk') is a source that was also used in early cell culture experiments. Zeatin is probably the most commonly occurring cytokinin in plants and has also been found in fungi (yeast) and bacteria. Other synthetic compounds, such as **kinetin** and **6-benzylamino purine** (**BAP**), show similar activity in being able to stimulate cell division.

An interesting illustration of the effect of cytokinins is seen in the infection of plants by the soil bacterium *Agrobacterium tumefaciens*, which causes the disease known as **crown gall**. The bacteria enter the plant through wounds and the plant cells are stimulated to divide forming a disorganised mass of tissue or tumour. The bacterial cell contains a plasmid (a small loop of DNA)

Figure 3.3 Plant tissue culture on nutrient agar in a petri dish. Growing cultures can be subcultured repeatedly and stored at low temperatures

Figure 3.4 At a later stage, shoots and leaves emerge and the plants can be grown on for the market as required

and genes on this plasmid can be integrated into the DNA of the plant chromosomes. During the infection by *Agrobacterium*, the host cells frequently incorporate the genes controlling synthesis of auxin and zeatin. These cells have thus become 'transformed' and even after the wound has healed, continue to proliferate due to their own supply of a cytokinin. This relationship between plant and bacterium has led to extremely valuable developments in gene technology. Other 'foreign' genes can be inserted into the plasmid and the bacterium acts as a *vector* for the transfer of genes from one plant species to another.

In the plant, cytokinins are found mainly in young meristems, such as the apices of roots and shoots, where cells are dividing rapidly. They appear to be transported along with water in the xylem though they have also been detected in the sap from phloem. Cytokinins are involved in the regulation of various processes in plants, including development (morphogenesis) of roots and shoots, development of lateral buds, cell enlargement, maturation of chloroplasts and a contribution to the processes that delay senescence. Their activity is linked to events in the cell cycle, in particular to nucleic acid metabolism and protein synthesis, though the mechanism of action is not known. The effects of cytokinins are often dependent on other growth substances, such as auxin, and may affect tissues differently at different stages of growth. As with gibberellins, evidence for cytokinin activities comes mainly from exogenous application to excised (cut) sections of plant material.

Abscisic acid

The effects of **abscisic acid** (**ABA**) are generally to inhibit or alter growth of plants, often linked with conditions of environmental stress. Abscisic acid was first associated with **abscission** (cutting off) of leaves at leaf fall and of ripe fruits. Since its chemical identification in the 1960s, it is now known that ABA is involved in a wider range of plant processes including dormancy in seeds and buds and closure of stomata in times of water deficit. Abscisic acid has been detected in organs throughout the plant and is transported in both the xylem and phloem.

Dormancy in seeds and buds of woody plants is an important adaptation for survival through unfavourable conditions, particularly cold temperatures. Concentration of ABA is usually higher in dormant seeds compared with seeds that are not dormant. It is probably the balance between ABA as an inhibitor and cytokinins and gibberellins as growth promoters which is responsible for the transition from dormancy to germination. One effect of ABA may be to inhibit the synthesis of hydrolytic enzymes which allow the breakdown of storage reserves in the seed, whereas GA_3 (gibberellic acid) appears to stimulate the release of α–amylase from the aleurone layer (see page 127).

ABA also appears to inhibit **growth** which is promoted by auxin and here the mechanism of action may be to block H^+ secretion thus interfering with the loosening of the cell wall which would allow elongation of the cells (see page 56). In the geotropic response of roots, amyloplasts may lead to an accumulation of ABA on the lower surface resulting in an inhibition of growth on the lower surface.

Evidence for a link between ABA and **environmental stress** in a plant comes from the marked increase in concentrations of ABA that can occur in a plant subjected, for example, to drought conditions. Application of ABA can induce rapid closure of stomata. Within the leaf, redistribution of ABA from the chloroplasts (where it accumulates) to the guard cells leads to change in turgor resulting in closure of stomata, thus reducing loss of water from the leaves. Plants may also lose their leaves (leaf abscission) as a response to water stress.

While ABA was originally associated with **abscission**, in most plants ethene may be the more important hormone whereas ABA is clearly linked with **senescence** (ageing). Segments of leaves, for example, turn yellow due to breakdown of chlorophyll and this process is accelerated by the application of ABA, whereas cytokinins antagonise the action of ABA and delay senescence.

Ethene (ethylene)

Ethene is the only gas known to act as a plant growth substance. Its effects were first recognised around the turn of the 20th century, when it was noticed that trees close to coal gas street lamps lost their leaves more than other trees, that bananas ripened prematurely when packed alongside oranges, and lemons would turn yellow when kept near heaters burning kerosene. Although the gas ethene was identified as being present in these situations, it was not until the 1950s that its importance in the metabolism of mature plants began to be understood.

Ethene is found widely in all parts of plants but at low concentrations. Because it is a gas, its distribution is by diffusion rather than direct transport. It can show a marked rise in some fruits (such as tomatoes, apples and avocados) during the ripening process. This is associated with a similar rise in respiration rate, measured by carbon dioxide output. Ethene is synthesised from the amino acid methionine, and it appears that the final step in the pathway is critical for controlling the concentrations of ethene present. A number of factors affect this final step, including environmental stress (drought, flooding, chilling or pollution), wounding or other plant growth substances. Ethene is known to be involved in certain responses to stress such as abscission and healing of wounds, as well as the ripening process. Auxin appears to stimulate ethene synthesis.

The process of **abscission** in leaves, flowers or fruits, is linked to the differentiation of a layer of cells known as the abscission layer. The cell walls become weakened due to the activity of enzymes, such as cellulase acting on cellulose and polygalacturonase (PG) on pectic substances. Ethene appears to promote abscission whereas auxin prevents it. Part of the ripening process in fruits involves similar softening of tissues, as illustrated by the change from firmness to mushiness in ripening tomatoes.

Ethene has a number of important commercial applications. It is generally applied as a compound which releases ethene, and is used to encourage ripening of fruits, as required for the market. Conditions for storage of fruits aim to reduce ethene production within the fruit and so delay ripening allowing longer storage times. Low oxygen and low temperatures reduce production of

QUESTION

Explain why you would *remove* an overripe or rotting apple from a box of home-stored apples, yet you might place a ripe banana into a box of unripe (green) tomatoes to help them ripen. Does the banana have any effect? How could you find out?

QUESTION

We might use the expression *factory gardening* to describe some of the practices adopted in the commercial horticultural industry. How important is micropropagation in contributing to the 'factory' concept in horticulture? Think about delivery of uniform products, timed to a predetermined marketing schedule and potential benefits of introducing new strains or varieties.

ethene, and certain substances such as potassium permanganate ($KMnO_4$) can be used to absorb ethene. In pineapple crops ethene is used to help synchronise flowering and setting of the fruit. Ethene can be used to break dormancy in seeds and buds, and promotes sprouting in potato tubers and bulbs.

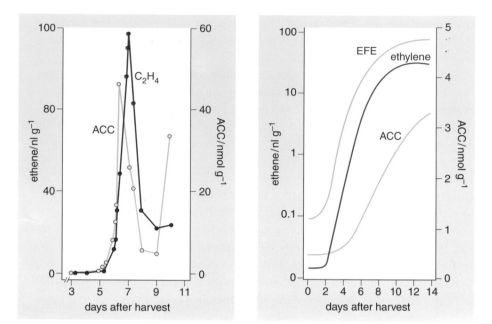

Figure 3.5 Changes after harvest in ethene and related metabolic events. Ethene is derived from the amino acid methionine, through an intermediate abbreviated to ACC. Ethene forming enzyme (EFE) converts ACC to ethene. Postharvest changes in ACC and ethene (C_2H_4) in avocado fruits picked from the tree (left). Postharvest changes in ACC, EFE and ethene in apple fruits (right)

Figure 3.6 Tomatoes are often harvested when green and firm, so that losses in handling are minimised and the tomatoes are not overripe when offered to the consumer. A ripe banana gives off ethene and this one could hasten the ripening of the unripe tomatoes in this bowl.

Photoreceptors

Photoreception is the detection of light and usually involves the absorption of light by a pigment known as a **photoreceptor**. Light is an important factor in the growth of plants as it not only provides the energy for photosynthesis and influences the direction of plant growth, but it has a direct effect on plant development. Some seeds need the stimulus of light before germination can occur. Light affects the formation of chlorophyll and the initial stages of growth, and it also affects the time of flowering in many plants.

If a plant is grown entirely in the dark, the whole plant appears yellowish-white in colour because no chloroplasts develop, the stem elongates more rapidly than normal, the leaves do not expand and the tip of the stem often remains in a hooked position. Such plants are described as **etiolated**: they are fragile and die as soon as all the food reserves in the seed are used up. In the early stages of seedling growth after germination, it is possible that etiolated plants are more suited to pushing their way through the soil, as sturdy stems and fully expanded leaves would offer more resistance. In addition, the rapid growth upwards towards a light source would be a competitive advantage.

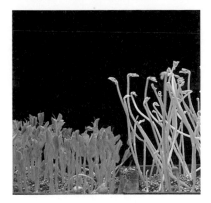

Figure 3.7 Etiolated cress seedlings (right) alongside normal plants

Some seeds require exposure to light before germination can occur. Imbibition, involving the uptake of water, must occur first, then the seeds become sensitive to light and need only a brief exposure to bring about the initiation of germination. Experiments carried out in 1937 on lettuce seeds, showed that exposure to red light of wavelengths between 600 and 700 nm promoted germination, but exposure to far-red light of wavelengths between 720 and 760 nm inhibited germination. Subsequent investigations showed that the effect of exposure to red light was not reversed by putting the seeds in the dark, but the effect appeared to be cancelled by exposure to far-red light.

In an experiment, using a variety of lettuce called 'Grand Rapids', batches of seeds were soaked in the dark and then exposed to alternating periods of red and far-red light. The percentage germination was determined. Each period of exposure to light lasted for five minutes. As can be seen from the results, shown in Table 3.1, the wavelength of light to which the seeds were last exposed has the greatest effect on the percentage germination.

Table 3.1 *Effect of alternating periods of red and far-red light on the germination of lettuce seeds*

Treatment	Percentage germination
red	70
red/far-red	6
red/far-red/red	74
red/far-red/red/far-red	6
red/far-red/red/far-red/red	76
red/far-red/red/far-red/red/far-red	7
red/far-red/red/far-red/red/far-red/red	81
red/far-red/red/far-red/red/far-red/red/far-red	7

From these experiments, it was deduced that the light was detected by a photoreceptor, called **phytochrome**, later isolated and identified by Borthwick and Hendrick. Phytochrome is a blue-green pigment, present in very small quantities in the leaves of plants. It exists in two interconvertible forms, P_R and P_{FR}, which have different absorption spectra. P_R, otherwise known as P_{660}, absorbs red light of wavelengths in the region of 660 nm and P_{FR}, otherwise known as P_{730}, absorbs far-red light of wavelengths in the region of 730 nm. When P_R absorbs red light it is converted to P_{FR} and when P_{FR} absorbs far-red light it is converted to P_R. So red light converts P_R into P_{FR} and the absorption of far-red light reverses the effect of red light. Exposure to natural daylight on a sunny day is equivalent to exposure to red light, so there will be more P_{FR} than P_R in plants. P_{FR} is converted slowly back to P_R in the dark.

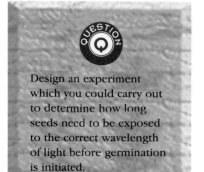

Design an experiment which you could carry out to determine how long seeds need to be exposed to the correct wavelength of light before germination is initiated.

Investigations on the phototropic responses of seedlings have shown that phytochrome is not involved. Experiments have indicated that the wavelengths of light which stimulate the phototropic response are in the blue region of the spectrum. However, there is evidence to suggest that phytochrome is involved in the unbending of the plumule hook in the stems of seedlings of French beans after germination and also in the initial expansion of leaves. These responses are similar to germination in that they appear to be triggered by a high level of P_{FR}.

As mentioned earlier, only a short exposure to light of the right wavelength is necessary to trigger germination in lettuce seeds, but much longer periods of illumination are required for leaves to expand fully and for the synthesis of chlorophyll. From a number of investigations, it has been shown that red light is more effective at inducing rapid responses, whereas far-red light is more effective in stimulating long-term responses. The explanation for this apparently paradoxical state may be that long-term responses require high levels of P_R or low levels of P_{FR}, or possibly that the level of P_{FR} has to be maintained within certain limits.

Photoperiodism and the initiation of flowering

In some plants, the day length, or **photoperiod**, has an effect on the induction of flowering. **Long-day plants** are induced to flower, or flower sooner, when the number of hours of daylight exceeds a critical value. In temperate climates, such plants usually flower in the summer. **Short-day plants** are induced to flower, or flower sooner, when the day length is less than a critical value. Plants of this type are found in temperate regions, where they usually flower in the autumn, or in the tropics where day length does not vary very much. Another group of plants are referred to as **day-neutral** as they do not appear to be affected by the length of the photoperiod. Examples of each type of plant are given in Table 3.2.

Table 3.2 *Long-day, short-day and day-neutral plants*

Plant type	Examples
long-day	henbane (*Hyoscyamus niger*), spinach (*Spinacia oleracea*), snapdragon (*Antirrhinum* sp.), cabbage (*Brassica* sp.), clover (*Trifolium* sp.), pea (*Pisum sativum*), petunia (*Petunia hybrida*), spring wheat, spring barley
short-day	soya bean (*Glycine max*), morning glory (*Ipomoea* sp.), cocklebur (*Xanthium pennsylvaticum*), rice (*Oryza sativum*), chrysanthemum, tobacco, strawberry (*Fragaria* sp.)
day-neutral	cucumber (*Cucurbita* sp.), tomato, maize, cotton

Temperature can also affect the induction of flowering and some plants require a period of chilling before flower formation will occur. Most spring-flowering plants in temperate regions show a stronger response to temperature than to short day length.

In a comparison of the importance of day length on flowering in spinach and chrysanthemums, it was observed that flowering in chrysanthemums was induced when the day length was less than 14 hours, whereas flowering in spinach was induced when the day length exceeded 14 hours. The transition between non-inducing and flower-inducing conditions of day length occurred at 14 hours. This is referred to as the **critical day length**. For spinach, the days needed to be longer than the critical length, but for chrysanthemums the day length needed to be shorter than the critical length.

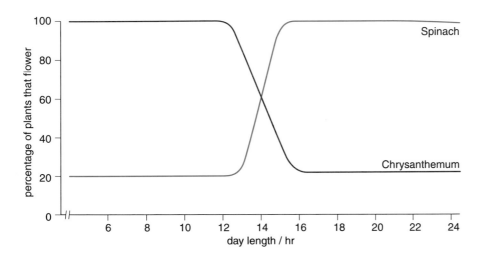

Figure 3.8 Comparison of day length and flowering in spinach and chrysanthemums

It has been shown that the extent of the dark period is more important than the day length, and we should really think in terms of long-night and short-night plants rather than short-day and long-day plants. If a long day is interrupted with a short dark period, there is no effect on the induction of flowering, but if a long night is interrupted by a short light period, flowering is induced in long-day plants and inhibited in short-day plants. So it would appear that the length of the uninterrupted dark period is important.

During the dark period, the amount of P_{FR} gradually diminishes as it is converted back to P_R. In short-day plants, when P_{FR} falls below a critical level, flower induction occurs. In long-day plants, low P_{FR} levels will inhibit flower formation, but a short light period in the middle of a long night enables P_R to be converted to P_{FR} and so increase in level. Long-day plants appear to require high levels of P_{FR} to initiate flowering, whereas in short-day plants, high levels of P_{FR} inhibit flowering.

Experiments carried out in the 1930s showed that the light stimulus required to induce flowering was perceived by the leaves. Flower induction in plants kept with their leaves in different day lengths from the shoot apices, can be

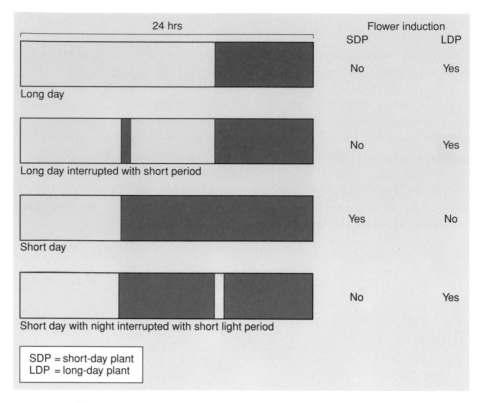

Figure 3.9 Effect of day length cycles on short-day and long-day plants

Figure 3.10 Perception of stimulus by the leaves

shown to occur when the leaves are in the appropriate day length. Even if only one leaf is exposed to the right conditions, flowering can be induced.

Such results suggest that an agent, other than phytochrome, may be involved in the transmission of the stimulus to the apex of the shoot where initiation of flowering occurs. The existence of a flowering hormone, named '**florigen**', was suggested, but this elusive compound has never been isolated. It is known that some plant growth substances, such as gibberellins and abscisic acid, have an effect on flower induction. Gibberellins can mimic the effects of red light and gibberellin treatment of lettuce seeds has resulted in germination. Stem apices of long-day plants treated with gibberellins have produced flowers, whilst short-day plants treated in the same way have not. Abscisic acid, a plant growth inhibitor, has been shown to affect flowering in long-day plants. Perhaps the mythical 'florigen' is a plant growth substance which has yet to be discovered or possibly a complex interaction between several plant growth substances which no one has yet worked out.

Mammalian hormones

Hormones are secreted by **endocrine glands**. Unlike exocrine glands, which have special ducts transporting their secretions to the site of action, endocrine glands have no ducts and their secretions pass straight into the blood. The secretions, known as hormones, enter the general circulation, where they are transported to their target organs.

Most mammalian hormones belong to one of three major groups of chemical compounds:
- **amines** – such as adrenaline from the adrenal gland and thyroxine from the thyroid gland
- **peptides** and proteins – such as insulin and glucagon involved in the control of the blood glucose level
- **steroids** – such as oestrogen, testosterone and the corticosteroids.

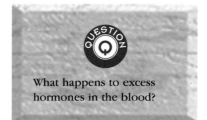

What happens to excess hormones in the blood?

Hormones may *promote* actions or they may have an *inhibitory* effect. They often affect one specific organ, referred to as the **target organ**, or they may have more widespread , diffuse effects involving several organs. A good example of the latter is **adrenaline**, which can affect the heart, the blood vessels and other glands. The secretions of many endocrine glands are under the influence of the **pituitary gland**, which plays a major role in coordinating the activities of the body.

Hormones are secreted in response to one of three types of stimulus:
- the presence, or change in concentration, of a specific substance in the blood, for example increase in blood glucose level triggers the release of insulin from the islets of Langerhans in the pancreas
- the presence, or change in concentration of another hormone in the blood, for example thyroid stimulating hormone from the anterior pituitary gland stimulates the thyroid gland to secrete the hormone thyroxine
- nervous stimulation involving neurones of the autonomic system, for example the release of adrenaline from the adrenal medulla in response to danger.

Hormones circulating in the blood only affect their target organs or cells because these will have the appropriate receptor sites or receptor molecules on their cell surface membranes. Protein and polypeptide hormones combine with receptor sites on the cell surface membrane and, once a hormone–receptor site complex is formed, another substance inside the cell, called the second messenger, becomes activated and has an effect within the cell. In many cases the **second messenger** is the nucleotide cyclic **AMP** (adenosine monophosphate). The hormone–receptor site complex causes the

CHEMICAL COORDINATION

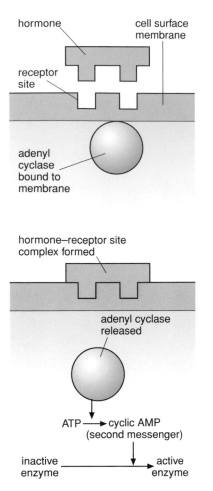

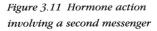

Figure 3.11 Hormone action involving a second messenger

release of adenyl cyclase from the membrane. This enzyme catalyses the formation of cyclic AMP from ATP. Cyclic AMP activates specific enzymes within the cell (Figure 3.11).

The steroid hormones work slightly differently by combining with the receptor molecules on the cell surface membrane and then, being lipid-soluble, the hormone–receptor complex is able to diffuse through the cell surface membrane and into the nucleus of the cell, where the steroid hormone activates a specific gene (Figure 3.12).

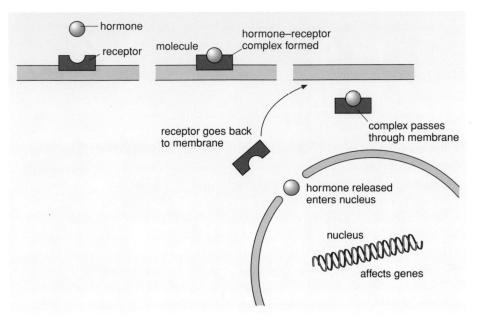

Figure 3.12 Hormone action of steroid hormones

Some hormones, such as insulin, affect the permeability of the cell surface membrane to other molecules. Insulin causes the cell surface membrane to become more permeable to glucose molecules.

The secretion of hormones in response to the presence, or increase in concentration, of another substance or another hormone is under the control of **feedback mechanisms**. In most cases, **negative feedback** operates, where an increase is detected, and a response is triggered which brings the level of the substance back to normal. This is shown clearly with the control of blood glucose level, where an increase in the level of glucose in the blood triggers the release of insulin, which causes the uptake of glucose into cells and leads to the conversion of glucose to glycogen, resulting in a decrease in the level of glucose in the blood. In some cases, **positive feedback** may occur: in the menstrual cycle, increasing levels of oestrogen cause the release of luteinising hormone from the pituitary gland.

The regulation of the glucose level in the blood

The normal level of glucose in the blood is about 5 to 5.5 mmol dm^{-3}. It is vital that this level is maintained so that all the tissues of the body receive a constant supply of glucose for respiration. It is also important that the level of

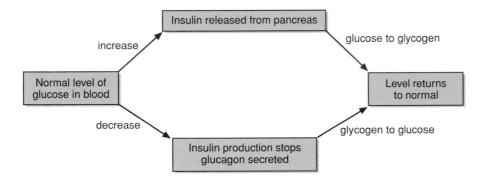

Figure 3.13 Negative feedback in the control of the blood glucose level

glucose in the blood does not rise too high, as this would affect the water content of the body. Under normal circumstances, all the glucose which is removed from the blood by ultrafiltration in the kidneys is reabsorbed in the first proximal tubule, so that none appears in the urine. If glucose is present in the urine – a condition known as **glycosuria** – the water potential gradient between the renal filtrate and the blood could be affected and water reabsorption would be reduced. If the glucose concentration of the tissue fluid is abnormally high, water would be lost from the tissue cells by osmosis.

A blood glucose level of below 3 mmol dm^{-3} results in a condition known as **hypoglycaemia**, inducing feelings of nausea, loss of concentration and cold sweats, leading eventually to loss of consciousness (coma). **Hyperglycaemia** results if the blood glucose level rises above 10 mmol dm^{-3} and glucose appears in the urine. This is accompanied by a fall in the pH of the blood and eventually leads to coma as well. Both hypoglycaemia and hyperglycaemia can occur in people with diabetes mellitus.

Variations in blood glucose level occur for a number of reasons. In humans, the level of blood glucose will show slight variations over a 24 hour period, rising slightly after meals but dropping again to a more or less constant level. The fall in level overnight or after a period of fasting is only slight. If a person is unable to synthesise insulin because of a lack of insulin-secreting cells in the pancreas, then the glucose produced as a result of the digestion of carbohydrates is not taken up and converted to glycogen for storage. In addition, there is no regulation of glucagon release and so any glycogen is broken down to produce glucose, resulting in very high levels of glucose in the blood. This condition is called **Type I** or **insulin-dependent diabetes mellitus** as it can be controlled by administering insulin. It develops in young people, so may be referred to as **juvenile-onset diabetes**. There is some evidence to suggest that this type of diabetes may be due to a viral infection initiating an antibody reaction which causes the destruction of the β cells in the islets in the pancreas which are responsible for the secretion of insulin. It appears that an inherited predisposition to this condition may be involved.

Type II or **insulin-independent diabetes** may also cause variations in blood glucose levels, but this condition is not due to a lack of insulin-secreting cells in the pancreas. It appears to be linked with the ageing process, hence the

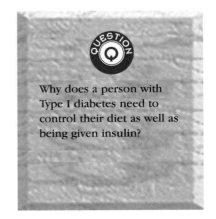

Why does a person with Type I diabetes need to control their diet as well as being given insulin?

alternative name of **mature-onset diabetes**. There is some evidence to suggest that this condition may also be inherited. In some cases the levels of insulin and blood glucose are both high, suggesting that a high dietary intake of glucose leads to a high level of insulin secretion. This pattern is often linked with obesity and can be successfully treated by controlling the level of carbohydrates in the diet, which in turn reduces both the glucose and insulin levels in the blood. In other cases, the level of glucose is high but low amounts of insulin are present, suggesting that the insulin-secreting cells do not respond to the levels of glucose in the blood or that their ability to secrete insulin is reduced. In such cases, drugs can be taken to stimulate insulin secretion.

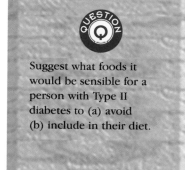

QUESTION

Suggest what foods it would be sensible for a person with Type II diabetes to (a) avoid (b) include in their diet.

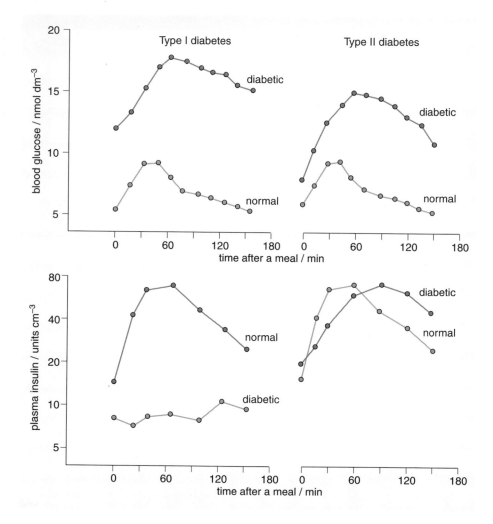

Figure 3.14 Glucose and insulin levels in the blood of Type I and Type II individuals compared with normal levels. Levels were measured at half-hourly intervals after eating a meal

Insulin

Insulin is secreted from the β cells of the islets of Langerhans in the pancreas in response to an *increase* in the level of glucose in the blood. It is a peptide molecule, consisting of 51 amino acids. The primary structure was worked out by Sanger in 1950. Insulin is secreted into the blood where it circulates in the plasma and affects all organs of the body. It binds to receptors on cell surface membranes, altering the permeability of the membrane to glucose and affecting enzyme systems within the cells. There are three main target organs for insulin:

- the liver where glycogenesis (conversion of glucose to glycogen) is stimulated
- muscle tissue, where glycogenesis is also stimulated
- adipose (fat storage) cells, where breakdown of lipids is prevented.

In addition, gluconeogenesis (breakdown of glycogen to glucose) in the liver is inhibited and the uptake of amino acids into cells is promoted. All these events lead to a *reduction* in the level of glucose in the blood.

Glucagon

Glucagon is a peptide made up of 29 amino acids and is produced by the α cells in the islets of Langerhans in the pancreas. It is antagonistic to insulin and is secreted in response to a *fall* in the level of glucose in the blood. The release of glucagon is inhibited by insulin and if insulin is absent, more glucagon is released. A balance between the two hormones exists, ensuring that glucose is released when levels in the blood are low. Glucagon affects the liver cells, promoting the breakdown of glycogen by activating the relevant enzymes. Glucagon also stimulates the uptake of amino acids and glycerol into the liver, where conversion to glucose occurs.

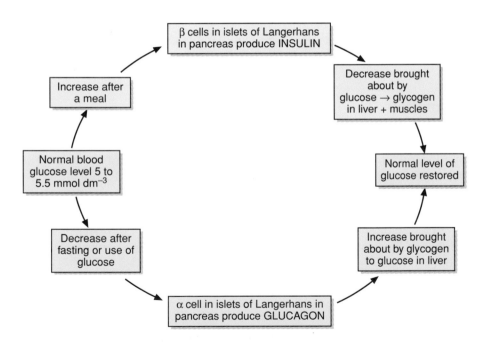

Figure 3.15 The control of the blood glucose level by insulin and glucagon

Cortisol

As glycogen reserves in the body are limited, fats and proteins may need to be converted to glucose to maintain metabolic requirements for energy release. A glucocorticoid hormone, called cortisol, secreted from the adrenal cortex, can stimulate the conversion of fats and proteins to glucose. This is especially useful to the body during periods of stress due to anxiety or disease. This

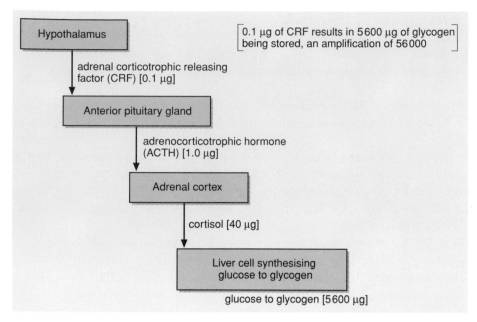

Figure 3.16 Cascade effect and cortisol production

hormone is part of a control mechanism, involving a **cascade effect**, where small amounts of one hormone stimulate the release of larger amounts of a *second* hormone, which in its turn stimulates even more of a *third* hormone.

The concentration of cortisol in the blood has a negative feedback effect on the secretion of ACTH (adrenocorticotrophic hormone) from the pituitary gland.

Adrenaline

Adrenaline, secreted by the adrenal medulla, also has an effect on the glucose level in the blood. This hormone prepares the body for action in stressful situations and its effects are widespread. One effect is to trigger the conversion of glycogen to glucose in the liver, so increasing the level of glucose in the blood should increased muscular contraction occur.

Details of the production and effects of the reproductive hormones and of antidiuretic hormone are dealt with in Chapter 1 (antidiuretic hormone) and Chapter 6 (reproductive hormones).

Nervous coordination in mammals

The nervous and endocrine systems perform the function of communication, and coordinate all the different actions of cells, tissues and organs within the body. The nervous system consists of the brain, spinal cord and peripheral nerves, and is organised to detect changes in both the external and the internal environment, to evaluate this information, and to make the appropriate responses. In this chapter we look at the organisation of the nervous system, transmission of the nerve impulse, and focus on the structure and functions of the central nervous system

Organisation of the nervous system

The nervous system is very complex and in order to help to understand the way in which it functions, it is often subdivided into several smaller systems, as shown in Figure 4.1.

The **central nervous system** consists of the **brain** and **spinal cord**. It integrates sensory information from various receptors and initiates the appropriate responses. The **peripheral nervous system** consists of paired **nerves**, which arise either directly from the brain, known as cranial nerves, or from the spinal cord, called the spinal nerves. It is convenient to divide the peripheral nervous system into the afferent nervous system, which consists of all the afferent, or sensory nerve pathways, and the efferent nervous system which consists of the efferent, or motor nerve pathways. The efferent nervous system is further divided into the somatic and autonomic systems. Somatic nerves carry impulses to skeletal muscles, whereas autonomic nerves carry impulses to smooth muscle, the heart and glands.

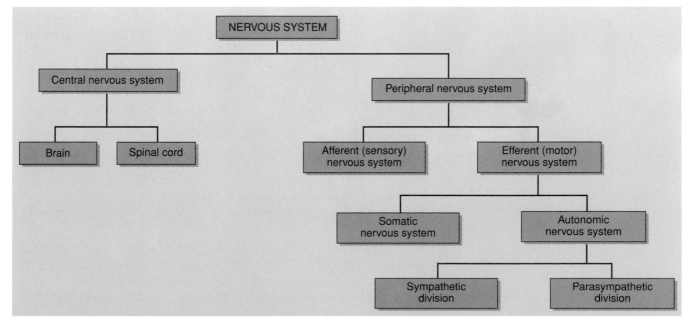

Figure 4.1 Organisation of the nervous system

NERVOUS COORDINATION IN MAMMALS

The entire nervous system consists of two main types of cells, **neurones** and **neuroglia**. Neurones are cells which are adapted to carry nerve impulses; neuroglia, which include Schwann cells, are cells which provide structural and metabolic support to the neurones. Neurones show considerable variation in size and shape, but they all have the same basic structure, as shown in Figure 4.2.

Each neurone consists of:
- a cell body, containing the nucleus, which is surrounded by granular cytoplasm, known as the perikaryon. The granules in the cytoplasm are referred to as Nissl substance and consist of dense clusters of rough endoplasmic reticulum.
- cytoplasmic processes which branch from the cell body – a single axon and one or more dendrites. The axon conducts impulses *away* form the cell body either to other neurones or to effectors, such as muscles. Dendrites are highly branched processes which carry impulses from specialised receptors, or from adjacent neurones with which they form synapses.

Although there is considerable variation in the size and shape of neurones, they can be classified into three main groups according to the arrangement of dendrites and axons. These groups are known as multipolar neurones, bipolar neurones and pseudo-unipolar neurones (Figure 4.2).

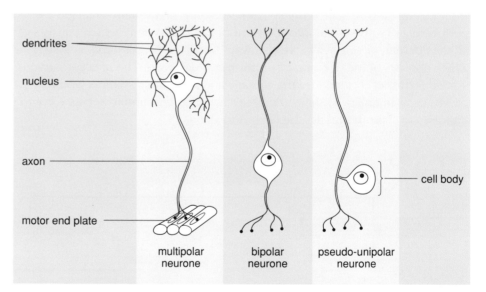

Figure 4.2 The three main types of neurone

- **Multipolar neurones** are the most numerous type and have many dendrites branching from the cell body. Typical effector (motor) neurones are multipolar.
- **Bipolar neurones** have only a single dendrite which arises directly from the cell body opposite the axon. These are relatively unusual neurones and act as receptors for the senses of sight, smell and balance.
- **Pseudo-unipolar neurones** have a single dendrite which, with the axon, branches from a common stem from the cell body. Typical sensory neurones are pseudo-unipolar.

In the mammalian peripheral nervous system, most axons are surrounded by specialised **Schwann cells**. During fetal development, the axon becomes enclosed by the cytoplasm of a Schwann cell, which progressively wraps itself around the axon. By this process, the axon becomes enclosed in a spiral layer of Schwann cell cytoplasm (Figure 4.3). The covering formed by the Schwann cell is referred to as the **myelin sheath**, and axons which are covered in this way are said to be **myelinated**. Between adjacent Schwann cells, there are short gaps where the axon is not covered by myelin. These gaps are known as the **nodes of Ranvier** (Figure 4.3).

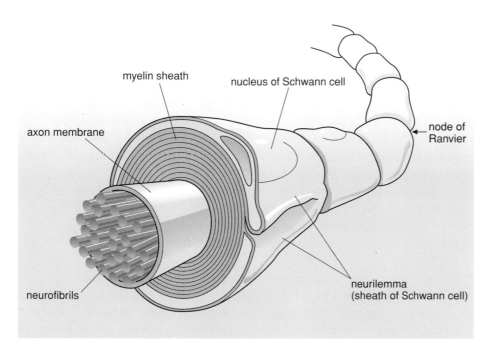

Figure 4.3 Transverse section of an axon and its coverings formed by the Schwann cell

The speed of conduction of the nerve impulse – the conduction velocity – is proportional to the diameter of the axon, which varies between about 1 and 20 µm. As a general rule, as the diameter increases, the conduction velocity also increases. However, in a myelinated axon, the conduction velocity is considerably faster than in a non-myelinated axon of the same diameter.

The nerve impulse

In order to understand the nature of the nerve impulse, we need to look at the concentrations of different ions inside and outside the axon. Each nerve impulse involves the movement of ions through the axon membrane. During the passage of an impulse, sodium ions move into the axon and potassium ions move out. When a neurone is not conducting an impulse, it is said to be in the **resting state**, and the inside of the axon membrane has a negative electrical change – the resting potential – relative to the outside. However, when positively charged sodium ions enter, the inside briefly becomes positive, or **depolarised**, generating an action potential. When potassium ions move out, the inside becomes negative again and the resting potential is restored.

NERVOUS COORDINATION IN MAMMALS

In the resting state, the resting potential is due to the overall effect of differences in the concentrations of ions across the axon membrane. These ions include sodium, potassium, chloride and large negatively charged organic ions. The concentration of sodium ions is much greater outside than inside, but in the case of potassium ions, the reverse is true. Chloride ions are more concentrated outside than inside and the large negatively charged organic ions are exclusively on the inside. These differences in the concentrations of ions are due to the permeability of the axon membrane to these ions. In the resting state, the permeability of the membrane to potassium is relatively high, due to the presence of protein channels, or 'gates' in the membrane which allow potassium ions to pass through. However, there are no gates which allow the negatively charged organic ions to pass through, so these remain trapped on the inside. The large ions are the main source of the negative charge on the inside of the axon. Although potassium ions can escape, relatively few of them do so. The tendency for potassium to move out, by diffusion, is countered because they will be attracted back in by the overall negative charge on the inside. This results in most of the potassium remaining on the inside. The concentration gradient for chloride is inwards, but remember that since the inside is negatively charged, chloride ions will be repelled. Sodium ions have a high concentration on the outside, and would be expected to be attracted inwards by the negative internal potential. However, the permeability of the axon membrane to sodium is relatively low and, although there is a slow inward movement of sodium ions, through sodium channels, they are captured by ion pumps and expelled to the outside.

When a nerve impulse is generated, the permeability of the membrane to sodium ions briefly increases, by the opening of more sodium channels, and sodium ions enter faster than they can be expelled by the ion pumps. As these positively charged ions flow in, the potential difference inside the axon rises to a positive value, known as the **action potential**. The permeability of the membrane to sodium then decreases, but this is followed by an increase in permeability to potassium ions, as more potassium channels open. This allows potassium ions to flow out and, as they do so, the potential difference inside the axon decreases to its negative resting value. The potassium channels remain open as the resting potential is restored and there is a slight 'potassium overshoot' which causes the membrane potential to become slightly lower than its normal resting value. This is known as **hyperpolarisation**, but the resting potential is gradually restored as sodium and potassium ions return to their resting concentrations. These changes in membrane permeability, and membrane potential are shown in Figure 4.4.

The changes described occur in a small segment on the axon membrane, but remember that a nerve impulse is a propagated action potential which moves at a constant velocity along the axon membrane. In a myelinated axon, however, the action potential 'jumps' from one node of Ranvier to the next. This type of conduction is known as saltatory conduction and greatly increases the conduction velocity.

During the passage of a nerve impulse, the axon has gained sodium ions and lost potassium ions. These ions are re-exchanged by sodium–potassium pumps which actively pump sodium ions out and potassium ions into the axon.

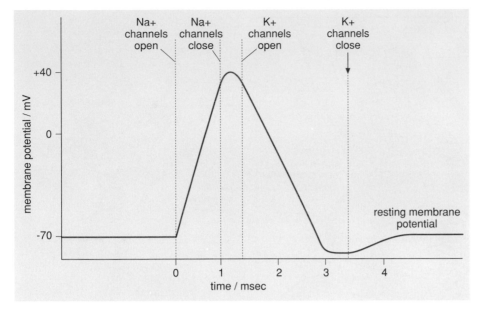

Figure 4.4 *The action potential*

The synapse

It has been estimated that there are over 10^{12} neurones in the human central nervous system, yet none of these neurones is in direct contact with other neurones. The impulse passes from one neurone to another across specialised junctions, known as **synapses**. There are two main types of synapses in nervous systems: electrical and chemical. In an electrical synapse, the membranes of the two adjacent neurones are so close, approximately 2 nm, that the wave of electrical excitation can pass directly from one neurone to the next. However, in most synapses, the gap is about 20 nm, and this is too large for direct electrical excitation. In these chemical synapses, the arrival of an impulse in the presynaptic neurone triggers the release of a chemical transmitter substance.

The mechanism of chemical synaptic transmission is summarised below.

1 An action potential reaches the synaptic knob of the presynaptic neurone and calcium channels in its membrane open to allow calcium ions to diffuse into the knob.

2 The increase in the intracellular concentration of calcium stimulates the movement of vesicles, containing a transmitter substance, towards the presynaptic membrane.

3 These vesicles fuse with the membrane and release their transmitter substance, by exocytosis, into the synaptic cleft. Each vesicle contains about 10 000 molecules of transmitter substance.

4 The transmitter substance rapidly diffuses across the synaptic cleft and binds to receptors on the postsynaptic membrane, which causes specific ion channels in the membrane to open.

5 The subsequent movement of ions, such as Na^+, K^+ or Cl^-, in or out of the postsynaptic neurone results in the generation of a **postsynaptic potential**. Depending upon which ions move, the postsynaptic membrane may be temporarily depolarised, or the inside of the membrane may become more negative than its normal resting value, in which case it is said

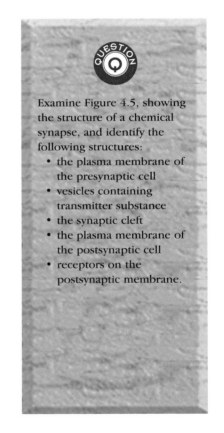

Examine Figure 4.5, showing the structure of a chemical synapse, and identify the following structures:
- the plasma membrane of the presynaptic cell
- vesicles containing transmitter substance
- the synaptic cleft
- the plasma membrane of the postsynaptic cell
- receptors on the postsynaptic membrane.

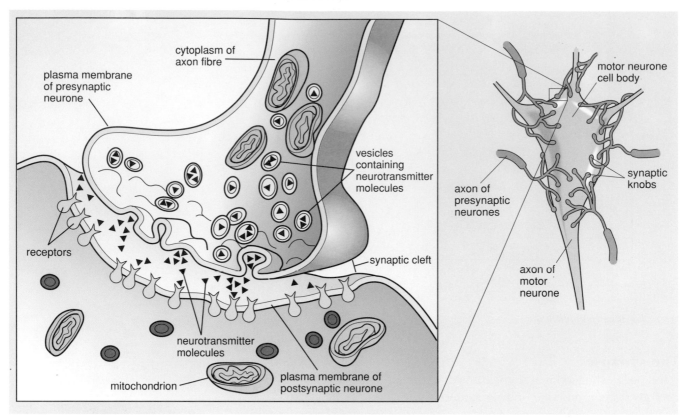

Figure 4.5 Structure of a chemical synapse

to be **hyperpolarised**. Depolarisation of the membrane results in the development of an excitatory postsynaptic potential; hyperpolarisation results in the development of an inhibitory postsynaptic potential.

6 The transmitter substance is quickly removed from the receptors, partly by diffusion and partly by enzyme action which breaks down the transmitter substance into inactive products.

There are many different transmitter substances within the nervous system, and they can be classified into four main groups according to their chemical nature. Examples of some of these transmitter substances and their functions are shown in Table 4.1.

Table 4.1 *Examples of transmitter substances*

Transmitter substance	Function
acetylcholine	transmitter substance at neuromuscular junctions and in many parts of the brain
amines, e.g. noradrenaline	transmitter in the sympathetic division of the autonomic nervous system and in several parts of the central nervous system
amino acids, e.g. glycine	an inhibitory transmitter substance in nerve pathways in the spinal cord
neuropeptides, e.g. endorphins	present in several regions of the brain, act like opiates to block pain

Many drugs and other substances act directly on the synapse and affect synaptic transmission. Such substances include nicotine, caffeine and opiates. Opiates are a group of substances which includes morphine, codeine and heroin. The effects of these substances are outlined below.

- **Nicotine** has a similar effect to acetylcholine at some synapses, having an excitatory effect on the postsynaptic cell. In large concentrations, nicotine can block synaptic transmission after initial stimulation.
- **Caffeine** inhibits the action of an enzyme, phosphodiesterase, resulting in an increased intracellular concentration of cyclic AMP. This can result in the release of increased amounts of excitatory transmitter substances in the brain and has a mild stimulatory effect, increasing alertness.
- **Opiates** act on the brain by binding to specific receptors thus reducing the response to painful stimuli.

The central nervous system

The brain, spinal cord and spinal reflexes

The brain develops from a structure in the early embryo known as the **neural plate**, from which folds arise, fuse, and form the **neural tube**. The anterior end of this tube expands to form the three main parts of the brain, referred to as the **forebrain**, **midbrain**, and **hindbrain**.

These three main areas subdivide to form the different regions of the adult brain, as shown in Table 4.2.

Table 4.2 *Main adult derivatives of the early brain. The brainstem comprises the midbrain, pons and medulla oblongata*

Early brain	Adult derivatives
forebrain	left and right cerebral hemispheres, hypothalamus
midbrain	midbrain
hindbrain	pons, cerebellum and medulla oblongata

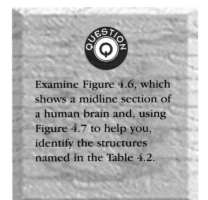

Examine Figure 4.6, which shows a midline section of a human brain and, using Figure 4.7 to help you, identify the structures named in the Table 4.2.

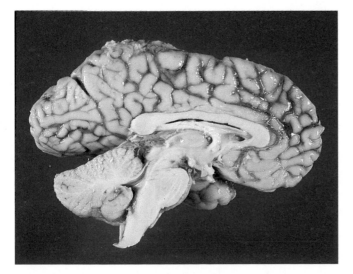

Figure 4.6 Midline section of a human brain

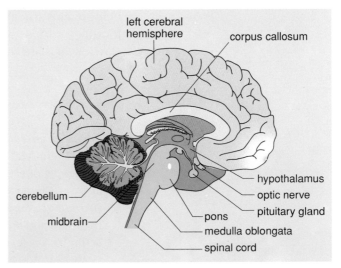

Figure 4.7 Diagram of a section of a brain to show the major structures

Table 4.3 *Functions of the main areas of the brain*

Part of brain	Main functions
cerebral hemispheres	The two cerebral hemispheres make up the **cerebrum**, the largest part of the human brain. The two hemispheres are connected by a mass of nerve fibres known as the **corpus callosum**. Functions of the cerebrum include: • receiving impulses from sensory receptors associated with the senses of heat, cold, touch, sight, hearing, taste and smell • initiating and controlling the contraction of skeletal muscles for voluntary movement • mental activities associated with consciousness, language and speech, emotions and memory
hypothalamus	• synthesises hormones secreted by the posterior pituitary gland • has an essential role in osmoregulation and maintaining body temperature • some neurones function as endocrine glands
midbrain	• conducts impulses between the hindbrain and midbrain • contains centres associated with visual and auditory reflexes
cerebellum	• acts with the cerebrum to produce skilled, coordinated movement of groups of skeletal muscles • coordinates activities associated with the maintenance of balance and posture of the body
pons	• consists mainly of nerve fibres which make a bridge between the two main parts of the cerebellum • contains nerve fibres passing between the cerebrum and the spinal cord • contains centres associated with the control of breathing (the pneumotaxic centres)
medulla oblongata	• contains nerve fibres passing between the brain and spinal cord • contains reflex centres associated with controlling the rate and force of the heart beat, the rate and depth of breathing and the diameter of blood vessels • contains centres associated with the reflexes of coughing, sneezing and vomiting

The detailed structure and organisation of the brain is very complex, but we can summarise the functions of the major parts, as shown in Table 4.3.

Ventricles and cerebrospinal fluid

Within the brain there are four large, fluid-filled spaces called **ventricles**. Two of the them, the lateral ventricles, are located one in each of the two cerebral hemispheres. The third ventricle is situated below the lateral ventricles and the fourth ventricle is situated below and behind the third ventricle, where the cerebellum is attached to the back of the brainstem.

The ventricles are continuous with the central canal of the spinal cord and are filled with **cerebrospinal fluid** (**CSF**). CSF is secreted mainly by structures known as choroid plexuses, networks of capillaries which project in to the roofs of the third and fourth ventricles. From here, CSF circulates within the system of ventricles and the central canal. It is reabsorbed back into the blood through arachnoid villi, which project into the venous spaces surrounding the brain. Functions of CSF include:
- providing a supporting cushion which protects the delicate structures of the brain and spinal cord
- acting as a reservoir of circulating fluid which the brain monitors for changes in the internal environment. For example, an increase in the carbon dioxide content of CSF will stimulate homeostatic control centres in the brainstem to increase the rate and depth of breathing.

Senile dementia and Alzheimer's disease

Each day, hundreds of neurones in the brain die as part of the normal process of ageing, but various diseases can greatly increase the loss of neurones. Such diseases are known as neurodegenerative diseases and these adversely affect the patient's personality, memory, attention span, intellectual capacity and motor control. The general term for this group of adverse effects is **dementia**. Alzheimer's disease is the most common form of senile dementia and affects approximately 700 000 people each year in the United Kingdom. Alzheimer's disease usually occurs after the age of 70, but occasionally at an earlier age. The cause of the disease is not known and there is, as yet, no cure. There are several distinctive changes in the brain which allow the diagnosis to be made; one of these changes is the accumulation of abnormal filaments, known as neurofibrillary tangles, within neurones. Other diseases of the central nervous system which result in progressive degeneration of neurones include Parkinson's disease, cortical Lewy body disease, motor neurone disease and Creutzfeldt-Jacob disease.

The spinal cord and spinal reflexes

The spinal cord is continuous with the medulla oblongata and lies within the vertebral canal of the vertebral column, or backbone. Thirty-one pairs of spinal nerves arise from the spinal cord and leave the vertebral column through spaces between adjacent vertebrae. In transverse section, the spinal cord is seen to consist of a central area of **grey matter** and an external layer of **white matter**. In the centre of the spinal cord, there is a canal, the central canal, containing cerebrospinal fluid (Figure 4.8).

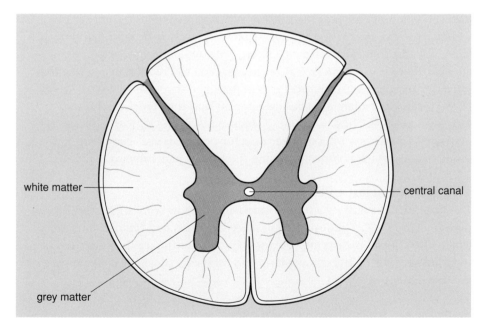

Figure 4.8 Structure of the spinal cord as seen in transverse section

The grey matter consists of the cell bodies of nerve cells, for example effector neurones which transmit impulses to skeletal muscles, and unmyelinated connector neurones, hence its grey appearance. The white matter contains columns of nerve fibres conducting impulses to and from the brain.

Spinal reflexes are the type of reflex action in which the effector neurone is stimulated by another neurone which originates in the spinal cord. This is called a connector neurone, because it provides a link between a sensory neurone and an effector neurone. The arrangement between the sensory neurone, the connector neurone, and the effector neurone forms the basis of a reflex arc, illustrated in Figure 4.9.

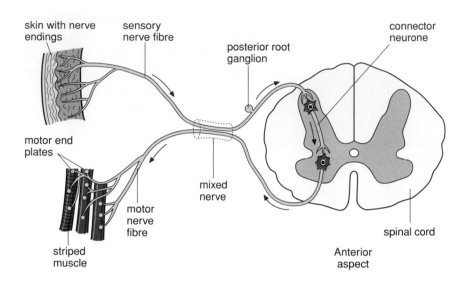

Figure 4.9 A reflex arc

In this particular case, the diagram shows the arrangement between neurones involved in a reflex such as the response to a painful stimulus, arising from stimulation of receptors in the skin. **Muscle stretch reflexes**, including the knee jerk and ankle jerk reflexes, involve only two neurones, sensory and effector, there is no connector neurone. Tapping the tendon just below the knee cap stimulates stretch receptors in the quadriceps muscle of the thigh. These receptors initiate impulses which pass into the spinal cord along sensory neurones. These neurones form synapses directly with effector neurones. Impulses arising in these effector neurones are conducted to the same muscle, which contracts, causing the foot to kick forward.

The mammalian eye

The eyes are spherical structures located and held in bony sockets, called the **orbits**, of the skull. They are held in place by rectus and oblique muscles, which also control the eye movements. The wall of the eye is composed of three distinct layers, the composition and functions of which are summarised in Table 4.4.

Inside the eye is a biconvex, crystalline **lens**, located behind the pupil and held in place by **suspensory ligaments** attached to the **ciliary body**, which contains smooth muscle. The lens separates the eye into two chambers, the anterior chamber at the front containing a colourless, watery fluid called **aqueous humour** and the posterior chamber, which is filled with transparent, gelatinous mucoprotein called **vitreous humour**. Both the aqueous and vitreous humours contribute to the maintenance of the shape of the eye.

Table 4.4 *The layers of the wall of the mammalian eye*

Layer	Location and composition	Function
sclera	tough outer covering containing collagen fibres; front part is transparent forming the **cornea**	protects the eye and maintains the shape of the eyeball; cornea allows light into the eye and the curved surface refracts the light on to the retina
choroid	found between the retina and the sclera; contains numerous blood vessels and pigment cells; modified to form the pigmented **iris** at the front, which contains radial and circular muscles	supplies retina with blood; pigment prevents reflection of light within the eye; iris controls amount of light entering by altering the size of the **pupil**
retina	innermost layer containing photoreceptors, the **rods** and **cones**, together with neurones supplying the **optic nerve**	respond to stimulus of light by producing action potential, leading to production of impulses which are transmitted to the brain via the optic nerve

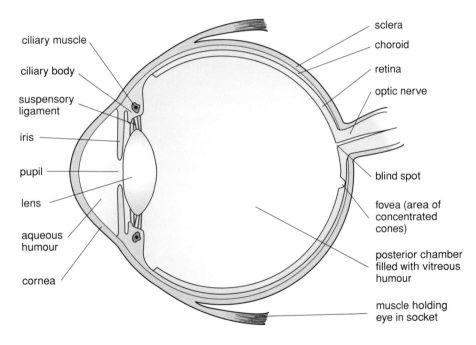

ciliary muscle
ciliary body
suspensory ligament
iris
pupil
lens
aqueous humour
cornea

sclera
choroid
retina
optic nerve
blind spot
fovea (area of concentrated cones)
posterior chamber filled with vitreous humour
muscle holding eye in socket

Figure 4.10 Vertical section through the mammalian eye

The eye is protected from mechanical damage by the bony ridges of the skull around the orbits and by the eyelids. There are **lachrymal glands** situated just above each eye. These glands secrete a watery fluid containing salts and lysozyme, a bactericidal enzyme. Blinking of the eyelids spreads this fluid over the surface of the eye, lubricating it and protecting it from abrasion and infection. The **conjunctiva**, a thin, transparent layer of cells, covers the front part of the eye, except for the central part of the cornea. This layer is continuous with the epithelium lining the eyelids and gives further protection to the exposed part of the eye.

The retina is made up of three layers of cells:

- the outermost, photoreceptor layer, containing rods and cones, both of which are partly embedded in pigmented epithelial cells of the choroid
- the intermediate, middle layer, containing bipolar neurones, which have synapses with the rods and cones in the photoreceptor layer and also with the ganglion cells in the inner layer
- the inner layer, called the internal surface layer, which contains ganglion cells and axons of the optic nerve.

Light entering the eye has to pass through the inner layer and the intermediate layer before it reaches the photoreceptor cells. Both the rods and cones are transducers, that is they convert one form of energy into another form of energy. In this case, light energy is converted into the electrical energy of a nerve impulse. Their functioning depends on the light stimulus being detected by a photosensitive pigment: **rhodopsin** in the rods and **iodopsin** in the cones.

Rods

Rods are distributed more or less evenly throughout the retina, but are absent from the fovea. They are sensitive to different intensities of light and are involved in vision at low light intensities. Their structure is shown in Figure 4.11. The outer segment contains the pigment rhodopsin, sometimes called **visual purple**, in flattened membranous vesicles, called **lamellae**. There may be up to 1000 of these vesicles in each outer segment, enclosed by an outer membrane. The outer segment is connected to the inner segment by a narrow region containing cytoplasm and a pair of cilia. The inner segment contains large numbers of mitochondria, polysomes and a nucleus. The mitochondria provide ATP for the re-synthesis of the rhodopsin. The synthesis of proteins for the production of visual pigment and the formation of the vesicles occurs at the polysomes. At the base of the inner segment is the synaptic region where the cell forms a synapse with a bipolar neurone.

Rhodopsin consists of a protein, **opsin**, combined with **retinal**, which is a derivative of vitamin A. Retinal can exist in two forms: a *cis* isomer and a *trans* isomer. Light causes the *cis* isomer to change into the *trans* isomer, which has a different shape and can no longer bind tightly to the opsin. This results in the splitting of the rhodopsin molecule into retinal and opsin.

A generator potential is produced, which causes an impulse to be transmitted along a sensory neurone. The initial stimulus in the rod cell causes hyperpolarisation, rather than depolarisation, because the outer segment membrane has a decreased permeability to sodium ions. Sodium ions continue to be pumped out by the inner segment and the rod cell becomes increasingly negatively charged.

Rhodopsin has to be resynthesised, using energy from ATP, but this takes time. Rhodopsin breaks down quite rapidly in bright light and there is not much of it stored in the rods. In bright light, eyes are light-adapted as the cones are used for vision and the rhodopsin in the rods is '**bleached**', in other words in the form of retinal and opsin. If a person goes from bright light into

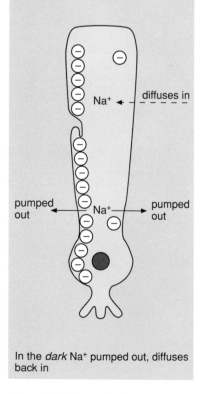

In the *light* Na⁺ pumped out, cannot diffuse in because membrane becomes impermeable. Inside of rod becomes increasingly negatively charged (hyperpolarisation)

In the *dark* Na⁺ pumped out, diffuses back in

Figure 4.11 Hyperpolarisation in a rod cell

dim conditions, vision is poor until enough rhodopsin has been resynthesised and the eyes become dark-adapted.

Cones

Cones differ from rods in the following ways:
- the outer segment is cone-shaped
- there are fewer membranous vesicles and they are formed from infoldings of the outer membrane
- they contain the visual pigment **iodopsin**, which is thought to occur in three different forms, each responding to light in a narrow range of wavelengths.

There are fewer cones than rods and they are more concentrated at and around the fovea. They are less sensitive to light, but more sensitive to the wavelength of light. There are three different types, one responding to red wavelengths, one to blue and one to green, involving different forms of iodopsin. According to the **trichromatic theory** of colour vision, different colours are perceived by the degree of stimulation of each type of cone by light reflected from objects.

Cones give greater visual acuity by enabling the formation of more accurate images than rods. Each cone synapses with a monosynaptic bipolar neurone, which in turn synapses with one ganglion cell. Several rods synapse with one bipolar cell, in this case referred to as a diffuse bipolar cell, giving rise to synaptic convergence. Vision is not as acute but the sensitivity is increased.

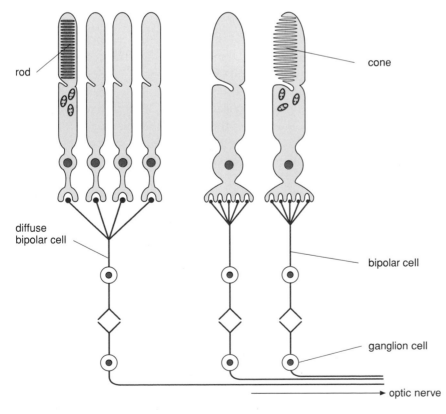

Figure 4.12 Synaptic connections in rods and cones

Mechanoreceptors in mammalian skin

Mechanoreceptors in animals are simple sensory receptors. Touch and pressure receptors are found in the dermis of the skin of mammals. Touch receptors, such as **Meissner's corpuscles**, are located just below the epidermis near the surface of the skin, whilst **Pacinian corpuscles** are deeper in the dermis and sensitive to pressure.

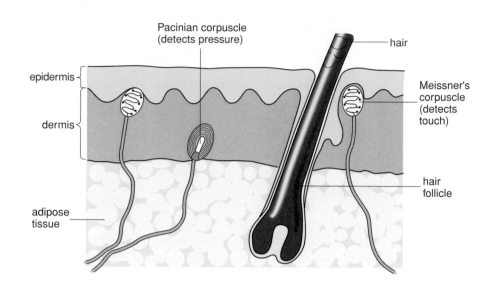

Figure 4.13 Mammalian skin showing location of touch and pressure receptors

Meissner's corpuscle consists of the end of a single neurone enclosed in a fluid-filled capsule. Stimulation results in a nerve impulse being transmitted along the sensory neurone to the central nervous system. In the more deep-seated Pacinian corpuscles, the end of the sensory neurone is surrounded by layers of connective tissue containing collagen fibres. In both types of mechanoreceptor, stimulation results in the receptor membrane being deformed, leading to an increase in permeability of the membrane to sodium ions, resulting in the production of a **generator potential**.

Support and movement

Supporting tissues in plants

Support in plants is provided by the **turgidity** of living tissues and the **rigidity** of lignified tissues. In herbaceous plants, such as buttercups (*Ranunculus* spp.), there is little lignified tissue and so turgid tissues play the major role in support. Woody plants, such as trees and shrubs, possess large quantities of rigid, lignified tissues which provide support. In all flowering plants, the nature and distribution of the supporting tissues in different organs is related to their situation and to the forces to which they are exposed.

The main supporting tissues in flowering plants are **parenchyma**, **collenchyma**, **sclerenchyma** and **xylem**. The first three are simple tissues, consisting of only one cell type, but xylem consists of four cell types, some of which have a conducting as well as a supporting function. Parenchyma and collenchyma are composed entirely of living cells, sclerenchyma cells are lignified and non-living and xylem contains both lignified cells and living cells.

Parenchyma

Parenchyma cells are unspecialised and make up the bulk of many organs in herbaceous plants. The tissue is often referred to as a 'packing' tissue but, although the cells may have a simple structure, they are metabolically active and important in the functioning of the plant. Each cell is almost spherical (isodiametric) in shape, with a thin cellulose cell wall, a large central vacuole containing cell sap and a thin layer of peripheral cytoplasm. When viewed under the light microscope, it is often impossible to distinguish the cell surface membrane or any organelles apart from the nucleus. When plant material is preserved, the living contents are disorganised, leaving only the cell walls visible. Air spaces exist between the cells, allowing for the diffusion and exchange of gases in respiration. When turgid, the cells push up against each other, providing valuable support in herbaceous stems and roots.

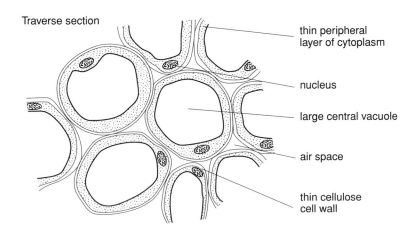

Traverse section

thin peripheral layer of cytoplasm

nucleus

large central vacuole

air space

thin cellulose cell wall

Figure 5.1 Parenchyma tissue

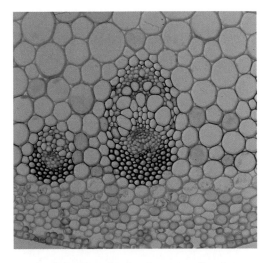

Section from the pith of a plant stem showing parenchyma tissue surrounding the vascular bundles

Parenchyma tissue is found in the cortex of roots and the cortex and pith of the stems. In these situations, the cells may contain stored starch in the form of starch grains. Parenchyma tissue is found in many storage organs, particularly the stem tubers of potato (*Solanum*), where the cells are packed with starch grains. The mesophyll tissue in leaves is a modified form of parenchyma. Palisade mesophyll cells are elongated, positioned just below the upper epidermis of the leaves and contain large numbers of chloroplasts. Spongy mesophyll cells, situated beneath the palisade cells, are more rounded, contain fewer chloroplasts and have large air spaces between them. Although their main function is photosynthesis, the turgidity of these cells is important in giving support to the leaf, so that it is held in the correct position to obtain the maximum available light.

Collenchyma

Collenchyma tissue is composed of living cells with extra cellulose in the walls. The cells are usually narrow and cylindrical in shape and may have pointed ends. In transverse section, they appear roughly hexagonal in outline and it can be seen that the extra cellulose is unevenly distributed, with more occurring in the corners. The cells are packed closely together with no, or few, air spaces between them.

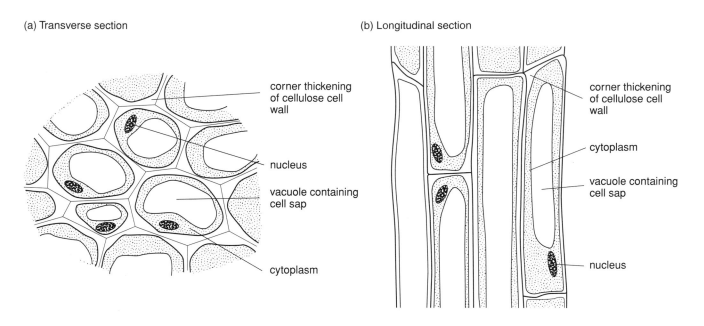

(a) Transverse section

(b) Longitudinal section

corner thickening of cellulose cell wall

nucleus

vacuole containing cell sap

cytoplasm

corner thickening of cellulose cell wall

cytoplasm

vacuole containing cell sap

nucleus

Figure 5.2 Structure of collenchyma tissue

Collenchyma tissue is important in providing flexible support in young plants, because it can grow and stretch as the plant grows. In herbaceous plants, it provides support in stems and leaves; it is not found in roots. In stems and petioles, it is usually located just below the epidermis, in the outer cortex. In ridged stems, it is usually collenchyma which forms the ridges and it is the tissue which is present in the corners of square stems such as white deadnettle (*Lamium alba*). In dicotyledonous leaves, collenchyma is found in the midrib region, providing flexible support.

Sclerenchyma

There are two types of sclerenchyma cells – **fibres** and **sclereids** – which differ only in their shape. Fibres are long, narrow cells with thick lignified walls and narrow lumens. They lose their living contents during development. The fibres have pointed, or tapered ends, which overlap and interlock with neighbouring fibres, forming a very dense supporting tissue with no air spaces between the cells. The walls contain simple pits, which are unlignified areas representing the location of groups of plasmodesmata in the primary wall. These pits do not serve any relevant function in the mature tissue.

(a) Transverse section

(b) Longitudinal section

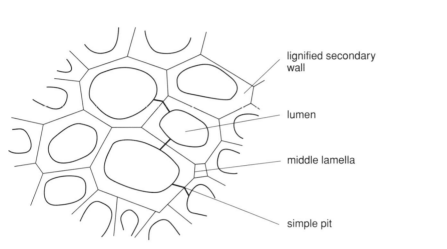
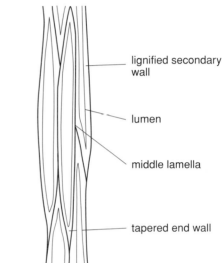

Figure 5.3 The structure of sclerenchyma fibres

Sclerenchyma tissue is strong due to lignification and the arrangement of the cells in sheets and strands within the plant. The tissue develops when growth in length of the organs is completed, so it is located in the mature regions of herbaceous plants. Sclerenchyma fibres are typically found forming the bundle caps in the stems of dicotyledonous plants and often form cylinders of tissue just below the epidermis of roots and stems. Fibres are also found in xylem and phloem.

Sclereids, often called stone cells, are more or less spherical in shape, but have the same thick, lignified walls as fibres. Living contents are lost during development. Sclereids often occur as isolated cells or in clusters in fruits and the testas of seeds. The gritty texture of the flesh of pear fruits is due to the presence of clusters of sclereids. Sclereids contribute to the firmness of tissues in which they occur.

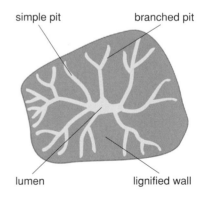

Figure 5.4 Sclereids

Xylem

Xylem tissue may be composed of four different types of cells: **tracheids**, **fibres**, **vessels** and **xylem parenchyma**. Tracheids, fibres and vessels become lignified during their development, losing their living contents.

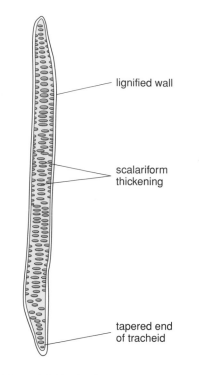

Tracheids are characteristic of conifer wood and vessels are found only in flowering plants. Both vessels and tracheids provide conducting tissue for water and mineral ions, as well as contributing to support. The fibres found in xylem tissue are very similar to those found in sclerenchyma tissue. They have no conducting function, but contribute significantly to the strength of woody tissues. Tracheids are elongated single cells with lignified walls and tapered ends. As they develop they lose their living contents, so the lumen of each cell is empty when mature. The thickening of lignin may take the form of rings, spirals, scalariform (consisting of interconnected bars of lignin) or reticulate (more interconnections than scalariform), similar to that found in vessels. Typically, tracheids have bordered pits, allowing the rapid transport of water from cell to cell.

Vessels are found abundantly in the xylem of flowering plants and are long tubular structures with lignified walls, formed by the joining of vessel segments, or vessel elements, end to end. The end walls of each vessel segment break down, leaving a perforation plate. The lignification can occur as rings, spirals, scalariform or reticulate as described for tracheids. The rings and spirals are typically found in the first-formed xylem, the **protoxylem**, whereas the reticulate and scalariform thickenings are more typical of the xylem formed later, the **metaxylem**. The rings and spirals allow for a limited amount of stretching which might occur in young structures.

Figure 5.5 Tracheid structure

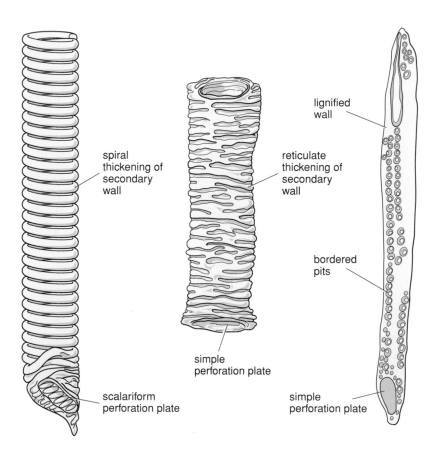

Figure 5.6 Vessel structure

Lignified cells give support because of the hard nature of lignin, but the distribution of the lignified tissues can play a role in withstanding the forces to which different plant organs are exposed. In roots, the xylem tissue is situated centrally and able to withstand tugging and pulling strains. In herbaceous stems, the xylem forms part of the vascular bundles, which are arranged peripherally in a ring in dicotyledonous stems, but are scattered throughout the cortex in monocotyledonous stems. In both cases, the xylem forms strands of supporting tissue, which withstand the bending strains caused by air movements or the passing of animals. Leaves possess an extensive network of veins spreading out from the midrib, providing support for the thin lamina. Again, the petiole and lamina of the leaf need flexible support, so that the leaf may be held in a position at right angles to the incident light.

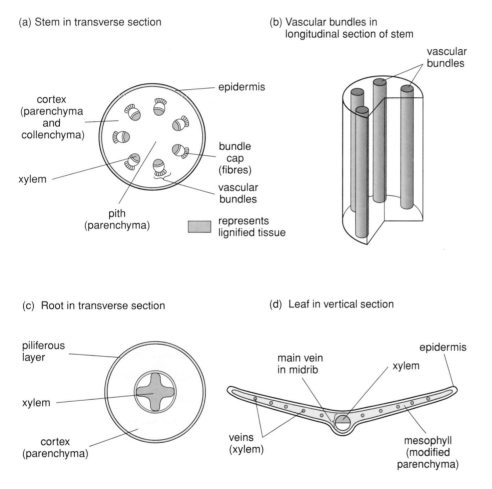

Figure 5.7 The distribution of supporting tissues in stems, leaves and roots of dicotyledonous plants

Skeletal systems in animals

Most animals possess some sort of supporting system, which may contribute to their shape, afford protection for internal organs and play a role in locomotion. Many skeletons consist of materials which have some rigidity and are resistant to compression, thus providing a framework for the body and helping to maintain its shape. Aquatic organisms gain some support from the water in which they live, but terrestrial organisms gain little support from the air and need to be able to support the body against the force of gravity. In order to provide for efficient locomotion, the body of a land-living animal also needs to be raised above the ground. Support is also provided for internal organs, which are attached to the skeleton.

Rigid skeletons, such as those consisting of bone or chitin, give protection to vital organs and also facilitate locomotion by providing lever systems and a place for the attachment of muscles. There is a wide range of skeletal systems, which can be grouped into three major types: **hydrostatic skeletons**, **exoskeletons** and **endoskeletons**.

Hydrostatic skeletons

Hydrostatic skeletons involve no rigid materials, but depend on contraction of muscles of the body wall against fluid in the body cavities. This type of skeleton is illustrated by the earthworm (*Lumbricus terrestris*), where the body consists of fluid-filled compartments, or segments. The body wall is composed of an outer layer of circular muscle and an inner layer of longitudinal muscle. Each segment is separated from its neighbours by septa, so that the fluid cannot escape and the volume of fluid is constant. The shape of the earthworm is maintained by the fluid pushing out against the body wall and the muscles of the body wall contracting against this incompressible fluid. This type of skeleton offers little protection to the internal organs, but does enable locomotion as the two muscle layers act antagonistically, bringing about changes in shape of the segments.

Why do organisms living in water often have less skeletal or supporting tissue than land organisms?

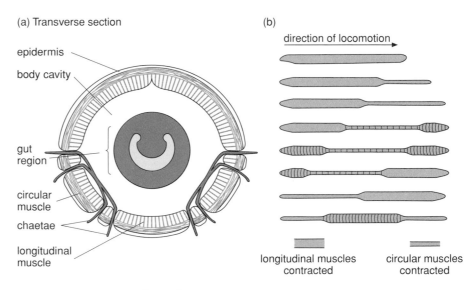

(a) Transverse section

epidermis
body cavity
gut region
circular muscle
chaetae
longitudinal muscle

(b)

direction of locomotion

longitudinal muscles contracted   circular muscles contracted

Figure 5.8 Locomotion in the earthworm

When an earthworm begins to move, the anterior segments move forwards due to the contraction of the circular muscles and relaxation of the longitudinal muscles. These anterior segments become longer and thinner. At this stage, the segments immediately behind are stationary, with both sets of muscles relaxed and tiny bristles called **chaetae**, extended, anchoring the earthworm in the soil. The wave of contraction of the circular muscles passes to this region as the longitudinal muscles in the anterior segments contract, making those segments shorter and fatter. These waves of contraction of the circular and longitudinal muscles pass down the earthworm from the anterior to the posterior, causing the body to move forwards. When either set of muscles is contracted, the chaetae are withdrawn so that the segments in that region can move without impediment, but in any region where the segments are stationary, the chaetae are extended providing anchorage. In this way, locomotion is achieved.

Exoskeletons

Exoskeletons are characteristic of members of the phylum Arthropoda and are mainly composed of **chitin**, which may be associated with other materials. Chitin is a long-chain polysaccharide very similar in structure to cellulose. It is made up of monomers of n-acetyl glucosamine, which differ from the glucose monomers of cellulose in that the –OH group of carbon atom 2 has been replaced by $-NH.CO.CH_3$.

Chitin is secreted by the epidermal cells and forms a hard, tough but flexible outer covering. It is often impregnated with other proteins, called **sclerotins**, and calcium carbonate to give added strength. This hard, outer covering gives very good mechanical protection to the internal tissues and organs. In many arthropods, particularly the terrestrial insects, there is also an outer, waxy **epicuticle** present, which prevents the loss of water by evaporation.

The exoskeleton consists of plates and tubes of chitin, joined together by flexible membranes of softer cuticle, so that movement is possible. In the appendages are hinge joints, operated by muscles attached to projections on the inside of the exoskeleton. A pair of **antagonistic muscles** – a flexor and an extensor – bring about movement. Contraction of the flexor muscle causes the joint to bend (flexion) and contraction of the extensor muscle brings about straightening (extension).

The obvious advantages of protection and support provided by the exoskeleton must be balanced against the disadvantage that such a skeleton does not allow for growth. Periodically, arthropods undergo **ecdysis**, when the old exoskeleton is shed and a new one is exposed. At first, this new exoskeleton is soft and flexible, so growth is possible, but it does mean that the animal is unprotected and vulnerable to predation and damage until the new exoskeleton hardens.

Endoskeletons

Endoskeletons are characteristic of vertebrates, but internal shells are found in some of the molluscs and structures composed of silica are present inside some protoctistans. Vertebrate skeletons are composed of **bone** or **cartilage** and located internally with the muscles attached outside. Bone and cartilage are living tissues and able to grow as the organism grows, so ecdysis does not occur. As with exoskeletons, joints are necessary to enable movement. Vertebrate skeletons have a wide variety of different types of joint, ranging from immovable joints between the bones of the skull to freely movable ball and socket joints at the hip and shoulder. The bones are held together in their

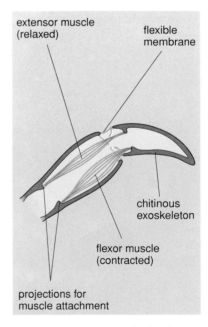

Figure 5.9 Movement in limb of arthropod

correct positions by elastic **ligaments** and muscles are attached to bones by inelastic **tendons**.

Movement is achieved by the action of antagonistic pairs of muscles. The limbs act as levers and at a hinge joint, such as the elbow or the knee, flexor muscle contraction results in flexing of the limb, while contraction of the extensor muscles brings about extension. At more complex joints, such as the shoulder or hip, other pairs of muscles allow sideways movement, allowing raising and lowering of the limbs. The mammalian skeleton will be considered in more detail later in the chapter.

Tropisms in plants

Plants respond to external stimuli, such as light and gravity, by means of growth movements called tropisms. The bending of seedlings towards a light source is an example of a tropism and is achieved by unequal growth of the two opposite sides of the stem of the seedling. Tropic growth movements are directed by an external stimulus. They are described as positive if growth is towards the stimulus or negative if growth is away from the stimulus. Thus shoots are **positively phototropic** but **negatively geotropic**, that is they grow towards light but in the opposite direction to the force of gravity.

Phototropism

Phototropism is the response of plant organs to the direction of light. It was investigated by Charles Darwin and his son Francis in 1880, using oat seedlings. When oat grains germinate, the stem apex is surrounded by a hollow protective sheath called the **coleoptile**. This structure covers the whole of the emergent part of the seedling and persists until the first leaf pushes its way through the top. Oat coleoptiles are convenient material to use because they can be grown easily in large numbers and they show the same responses as shoots.

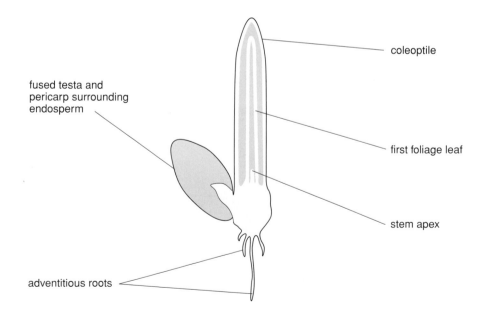

Figure 5.10 Oat seedling showing coleoptile

The Darwins observed that when oat coleoptiles were grown in conditions where they were illuminated from one side, the coleoptiles bent towards the light. The curvature occurred in the region of growth (elongation) just below the tip. They then removed the tips of the coleoptiles and showed that the response did not occur. In further experiments they covered the tips with opaque caps and also buried the coleoptiles, leaving only the tips exposed. In the first case, no curvature occurred, but in the second, it did. Darwin's investigations are summarised in Table 5.1.

Table 5.1 *Darwin's experiments with oat coleoptiles*

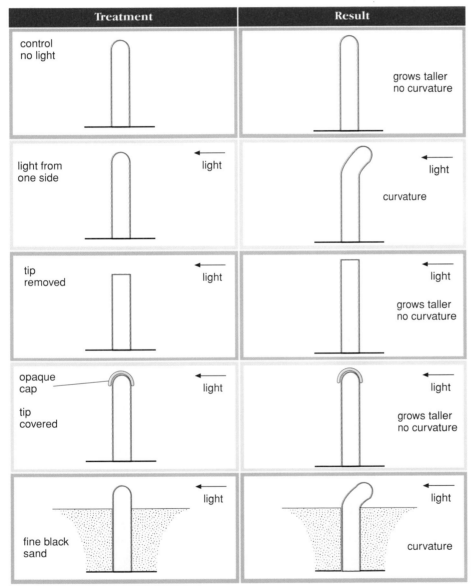

It was suggested that the tips of the coleoptiles were the 'sites of perception' and that some 'influence' passed from the tip to the region of growth, the 'effector'. In 1913, the experiments carried out by a Danish physiologist, Boysen-Jensen, provided further evidence that some kind of signal passes from the tip, where the stimulus is received, to the region of elongation where the response occurs. From his experiments, it appeared that the signal was likely to be a chemical substance. The signal was unable to pass through the impermeable mica plates he inserted in the coleoptiles. The signal also appeared to be produced on the shaded side of the coleoptile, suggesting that light affected its production or distribution (Table 5.2).

Table 5.2 *Summary of Boysen-Jensen's experiments*

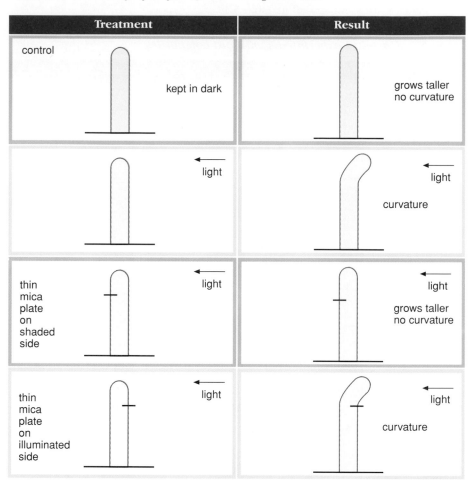

The existence of a chemical transmitter was proved in 1928 by Fritz Went, a Dutch physiologist. He cut the tips off oat coleoptiles and left them on agar for several hours, so that any substance produced in the tips could diffuse into the agar. He chopped up the agar into blocks and placed them on decapitated coleoptiles, some symmetrically and others asymmetrically. Control experiments were also carried out using untreated agar blocks. His experiments and the results are shown in Table 5.3.

Went also showed that exposing coleoptile tips to unilateral light resulted in more of the chemical transmitter being present on the shaded side than on the illuminated side, supporting the conclusions drawn by Boysen-Jensen. Went placed coleoptile tips on agar blocks divided in half vertically by thin metal plates. The tips were illuminated from one side. After several hours, each half block was placed asymmetrically on an oat coleoptile. It was seen that the halves that had received the chemical from the shaded side produced

Table 5.3 *Summary of Went's experiments*

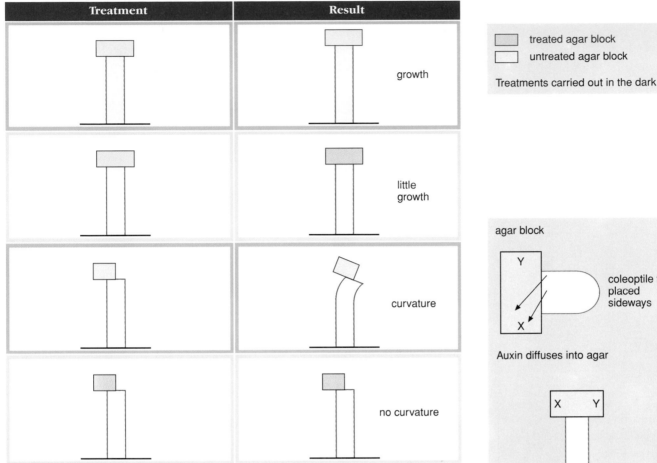

Treatment	Result
	growth
	little growth
	curvature
	no curvature

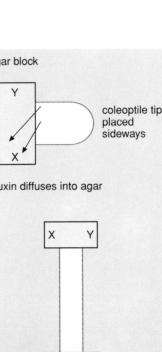

treated agar block

untreated agar block

Treatments carried out in the dark

agar block

Y

X

coleoptile tip placed sideways

Auxin diffuses into agar

X   Y

Block placed on decapitated coleoptile

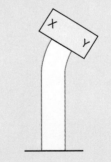

X

Y

Curvature results due to greater auxin concentration on the lower (x) side of block

a greater curvature in the coleoptiles than the halves which had received chemical from the illuminated side. The degree of curvature was directly proportional to the concentration of the chemical transmitter, a fact which has subsequently been used in the development of a bioassay technique for measuring the amount of chemical present.

The chemical transmitter was named '**auxin**' and later identified as **indoleacetic acid** (**IAA**). At the time, it was suggested that unilateral light causes auxin, produced at the shoot apex, to move to the shaded side, where the greater concentration stimulates cell elongation in the region just behind the apex, the zone of elongation. This causes the tip of the shoot to bend towards the light.

Geotropism

Roots and shoots show different responses to gravity. Roots are **positively geotropic** and grow downwards, whereas shoots are **negatively geotropic** and grow upwards. Went showed that gravity affected the distribution of auxin in coleoptile tips. He found that there was a greater concentration of auxin on the lower side than the upper side when the tips were placed horizontally. In intact coleoptiles, this greater concentration would stimulate cell elongation on the lower side, causing the coleoptile to curve upwards: a negative geotropic response.

Figure 5.11 Effect of gravity on the distribution of auxin in the coleoptile tip

It is easy to show that the roots of seedlings, such as peas, when placed horizontally will grow downwards, showing a positive geotropic response. A **klinostat**, consisting of a horizontal rotating chamber, can be used to eliminate the effects of gravity. The roots of seedlings, arranged as shown in Figure 5.12, will continue to grow straight whilst the chamber is rotated slowly, but will grow downwards when it is stopped.

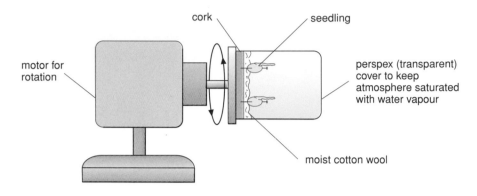

Figure 5.12 Pea seedlings on a klinostat

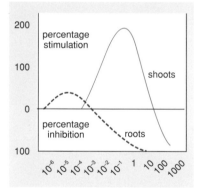

Figure 5.13 Effect of auxin concentration on cell elongation in roots and shoots

It is also easy to demonstrate that the root tip is sensitive to gravity, as decapitated roots do not respond to the stimulus. It is more difficult to show that the growth responses are due to the movement of auxin, or to extract auxin in any quantity from the roots.

Other experiments using auxin extracted from coleoptile tips were carried out to compare the effects of different concentrations of auxin on the curvature of roots and shoots. Results showed that high concentrations of auxin caused curvature in shoots but not in roots, whereas low concentrations caused curvature in roots but not in shoots. Results from similar experiments led to the hypothesis that roots and shoots show different sensitivities to auxin: *low* concentrations of auxin *promote* cell elongation in roots, but *high* concentrations *inhibit* cell elongation; in shoots, there is little response until the auxin concentration is high.

Starch statoliths and the geotropic response

In plants, the stimulus of gravity results in a tropic growth response towards the direction of the force – **positive geotropism** – or away from the direction of the force – **negative geotropism**. Roots are normally positively geotropic and shoots are negatively geotropic. The stimulus is detected by shoot and root tips, but there has been some discussion as to how the stimulus initiates a response. Observations made on root tips have revealed the presence of **amyloplasts**, containing large starch grains, in the cells of the root cap. The starch grains, referred to as **starch statoliths**, move in response to gravity and somehow cause a redistribution of growth substances, so that the cells on the upper surface of the root elongate and the root grows downwards. Similarly, it has been shown that stems also have starch grains, so the stimulus could be detected in the same way. It has been established that redistribution of auxin could account for the growth response in the shoot, but there is some doubt as to whether this is the case in roots, as the quantities involved are very small.

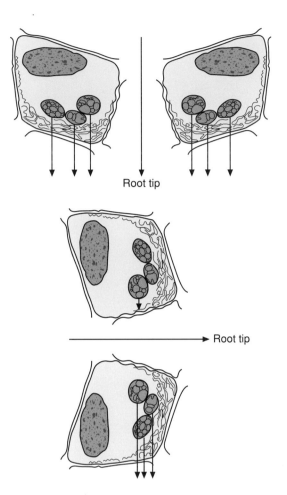

Root tip

Root tip

Figure 5.14 Starch statoliths and the detection of the stimulus of gravity

Work on maize seedlings has failed to show the presence of auxin in root tips, but the presence of **abscisic acid** (**ABA**), a growth inhibitor, has been clearly demonstrated. Experiments comparing the effects of abscisic acid and IAA have indicated that high concentrations of ABA will inhibit cell elongation and bring about curvature in decapitated maize roots, IAA had little effect.

ABA can be shown to be transported away from the root tips, to move in response to gravity and to inhibit growth, thus it is a more likely candidate than IAA in bringing about the geotropic response in roots.

Plants respond to touch by a growth response called **thigmotropism** (haptotropism). This can be seen in the garden pea (*Pisum sativum*), whose leaf tendrils will grow around any solid structure with which they come into contact. Another response to touch is seen in *Mimosa pudica*, where a light contact is sufficient to cause the leaflets of the leaves to fold together rapidly, followed by the drooping of the petiole. This is an example of a **haptonastic**

Table 5.4 *The effects of ABA on decapitated maize roots*

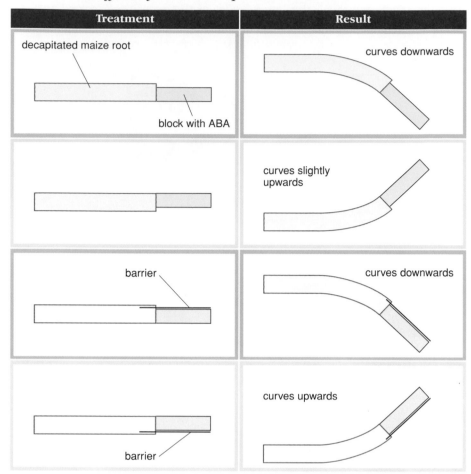

movement, involving sudden loss of turgor in cells at the base of each leaflet and at the base of the petiole. The stimulus is rapidly transmitted and it is thought that a hormone, which travels in the xylem, is involved.

Movement in animals

Movement in animals is achieved through the action of muscles. In considering the different skeletal systems earlier in this chapter, it was clear that locomotion is brought about by the action of pairs of antagonistic muscles. Movement within an animal can also be due to muscle action. The pumping of the heart is due to contraction of cardiac muscle and the movement of ingested food through the alimentary canal is achieved by smooth muscle contracting in a coordinated way in peristalsis.

Muscles are composed of elongated cells called **muscle fibres**, which can contract and relax. In vertebrates, there are three types of muscle: **striated**, **smooth** and **cardiac**. Their distribution, functions and general characteristics are summarised in Table 5.5.

Table 5.5 *Distribution and characteristics of muscle types in vertebrates*

Muscle type	Distribution and function	General characteristics
striated (skeletal, striped, voluntary)	attached to bones by inelastic tendons: concerned with locomotion, e.g. biceps, triceps muscles in upper arm	elongated muscle fibres with obvious striations; associated with large numbers of mitochondria; able to contract rapidly; fatigues easily; under the control of the voluntary nervous system.
smooth (unstriated, unstriped, plain, involuntary)	present in tubular organs of the body, e.g. gut, bladder, uterus, blood vessels; concerned with the movement of materials within the body	spindle shaped, uninucleate cells, with no cross-striations, held together with collagen forming layers; rate of contraction slow but can be maintained for long periods; needs no nervous stimulation, shows spontaneous rhythmic contraction; under control of the involuntary (autonomic) nervous system
cardiac	present only in the heart; contraction maintains the circulation of the blood	fibres with cross-striations; larger numbers of mitochondria than striated muscle; contracts spontaneously (myogenic); rate of contraction controlled by autonomic nervous system

Striated muscle, such as the biceps muscle in the arm, is made up of parallel, multinucleate fibres, which may be several centimetres in length and between 0.1 and 0.01 mm in diameter. Each muscle fibre is surrounded by a membrane, the **sarcolemma**, which is very similar in structure to a cell surface membrane. Within each muscle fibre are large numbers of **myofibrils**, with characteristic cross-striations, the **Z lines** or **Z bands**. These Z lines occur at regular intervals along each myofibril and the region between two Z lines, about 2.5 μm in length in a relaxed muscle, is called a **sarcomere**.

In the myofibrils, thin filaments of the protein **actin** extend from the Z lines into the sarcomeres on either side. In the centre of each sarcomere, the actin filaments are interspersed with thick filaments of another protein, **myosin**. The cytoplasm of the myofibrils is referred to as the **sarcoplasm** and consists of a network of membranes forming the **sarcoplasmic reticulum**. A system of transverse tubules, known as the **T system**, extends across the muscle fibre and is in contact with the sarcolemma. The actin and myosin filaments are cross-linked, and when contraction of the muscle occurs, the thin actin filaments slide between the thick myosin filaments, shortening the length of each sarcomere.

In the sarcomeres of each myofibril, the alternating light and dark bands, termed **I bands** and **A bands** respectively, correspond to areas of actin only (I bands) and actin and myosin together (A bands). Within the A band, a central zone, the **H zone**, appears lighter than the regions on either side. In this zone, there are only myosin filaments, but in the darker regions either

SUPPORT AND MOVEMENT

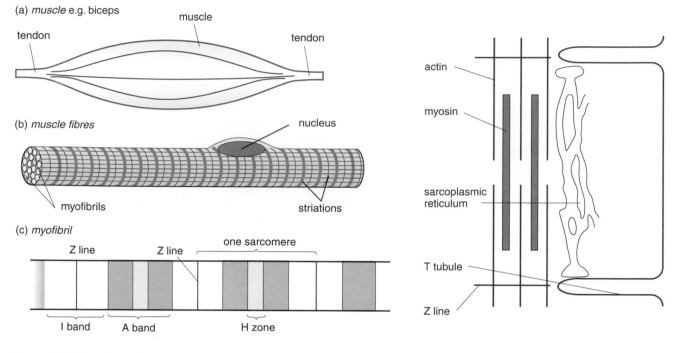

Figure 5.15 Striated muscle structure

side there is overlap of the actin and myosin filaments. Transverse sections through the myofibrils indicate that the myosin filaments are regularly arranged in a lattice formation and, where overlap with the actin filaments occurs, six actin filaments surround each myosin filament.

When contraction occurs, the I bands shorten and the H zones become narrower because the actin filaments are pulled in between the myosin filaments and there is a greater overlap between the two sets. As a result, the Z lines are drawn closer together and the length of each sarcomere shortens. It should be noted that the A bands always stay the same length.

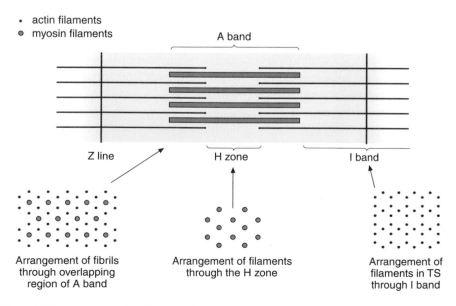

Figure 5.16 Arrangement of filaments in a sarcomere

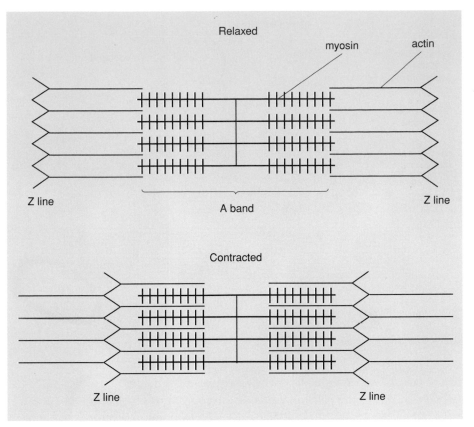

Figure 5.17 Arrangement of the thick (myosin) and thin (actin) filaments before and after contraction

Myosin filaments are made up of several hundred molecules of the protein myosin, each consisting of a long rod-shaped portion and a globular 'head'. The molecules are aligned along the filaments so that the heads face outwards in both directions, away from the centre of the filament, leaving a bare zone in the middle.

Actin filaments contain three different proteins:
- small globular molecules of actin arranged in two helical strands twisted around each other
- long, thin tropomyosin molecules, joined end to end, forming thin strands wound around the actin in the groove between the filaments
- globular molecules of troponin, a calcium-binding protein attached to each tropomyosin molecule.

When a muscle is stimulated to contract, a wave of depolarisation reaches the motor end plate at a **neuromuscular junction**. Acetylcholine is released into the synaptic cleft and diffuses to the sarcolemma, where it causes depolarisation. The wave of depolarisation then spreads into the system of transverse tubules, known as the **T system**. The membranes of the sarcoplasmic reticulum become more permeable to calcium ions, which are released into the sarcoplasm.

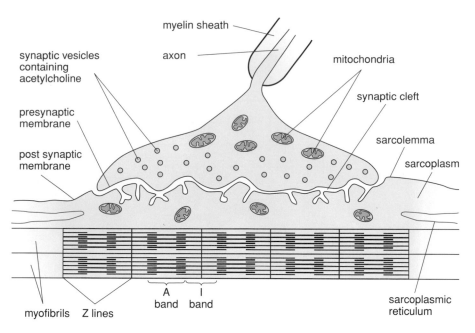

Figure 5.18 Motor end plate

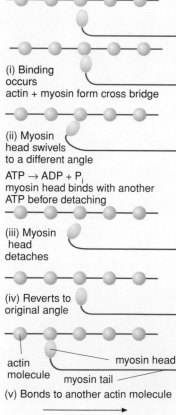

(i) Binding occurs
actin + myosin form cross bridge

(ii) Myosin head swivels to a different angle

ATP → ADP + P$_i$
myosin head binds with another ATP before detaching

(iii) Myosin head detaches

(iv) Reverts to original angle

actin molecule

myosin head

myosin tail

(v) Bonds to another actin molecule

Direction in which actin filament is pulled by this ratchet mechanism

Figure 5.19 Building of myosin to actin, forming cross-bridges

The release of calcium ions from the sarcoplasmic reticulum into the sarcoplasm causes the calcium ion concentration to rise. Calcium ions bind to troponin molecules in the actin filaments. The troponin molecules change in shape, allowing tropomyosin molecules to move out of their blocking positions, exposing the myosin-binding sites on the actin molecules. The heads of the myosin molecules link to the actin to form **actomyosin cross-bridges**. The myosin heads, which have molecules of ATP (adenosine triphosphate) temporarily bound to them, become attached to the actin at a certain angle. A cross-bridge is formed and the myosin heads then swivel to a different angle, using energy derived from the ATP. The actin filaments are moved towards the centre of the sarcomere. Each myosin head remains attached until it binds with another ATP molecule, when it detaches, reverts to its original angle and binds to another myosin-binding site on the actin filament. Calcium ions are actively taken back into the vesicles of the sarcoplasmic reticulum until the next wave of depolarisation arrives.

ATP is the immediate source of energy for muscle contraction as it is the only substance that the muscle proteins can use directly. In a resting muscle, only small quantities of ATP are present, probably only enough for eight to ten rapid muscle twitches. In an active muscle, ATP needs to be restored rapidly. This process involves **creatine phosphate**, which is present in the muscle in larger amounts. The adenosine diphosphate (ADP) released as ATP is used, is reconverted to ATP using phosphate from the creatine phosphate. Restoration of the creatine phosphate occurs by the oxidation of fatty acids or glycogen yielding ATP, which is then used to phosphorylate the creatine.

During muscle contraction:

$$ATP \longrightarrow ADP + P_i + \text{energy for contraction}$$

In order to restore levels of ATP:

$$\text{creatine phospate} + ADP \longrightarrow \text{creatine} + ATP$$

Creatine phosphate levels restored later:

$$\text{creatine} + ATP \longrightarrow \text{creatine phosphate.}$$

Figure 5.20 Maintaining the supply of ATP using creatine phosphate

The mammalian skeleton

The mammalian skeleton is an endoskeleton composed of bone and cartilage, giving the body shape and support and providing protection for the internal organs. It can be divided into the **axial skeleton**, consisting of the skull, vertebral column, ribs and sternum and the **appendicular skeleton**, made up of the limbs and limb girdles.

The **vertebral column** consists of 33 bones called **vertebrae**, modified to perform different functions in different regions. Typically each vertebra possesses:
- a solid disc of bone called the **centrum**
- an arch of bone called the **neural** or **vertebral arch**, enclosing and protecting the **neural canal**
- bony projections from the vertebral arch for muscle attachment, consisting of a dorsal **neural spine** and a **transverse process** on either side of the vertebral arch
- two pairs of articulating surfaces (facets), the **prezygapophyses** situated anteriorly and the **post zygapophyses** situated posteriorly.

The centra are the load-bearing parts and centra of adjacent vertebrae are separated by **intervertebral discs** made of cartilage. These discs act as shock absorbers and allow a certain amount of limited movement between the vertebrae. The prezygapophyses of one vertebra articulate with the postzygapophyses of the vertebra above it.

There are five different types of vertebrae in the vertebral column. The numbers of each and their location and distinguishing features are summarised in Table 5.6.

The vertebrae are attached to each other by ligaments. There is some flexibility, allowing bending and slight twisting movements.

The limb girdles provide a connection between the axial skeleton and the limbs. The **pelvic girdle** consists of two pelvic bones formed by the fusion of the ilium, the pubis and the ischium during the growth of the embryo. The pelvic bones are joined to each other by the pubic symphysis at the front (ventrally) and to either side of the sacrum at the back (dorsally). The upper leg bones articulate with the pelvic bones, forming a ball and socket joint with the acetabulum.

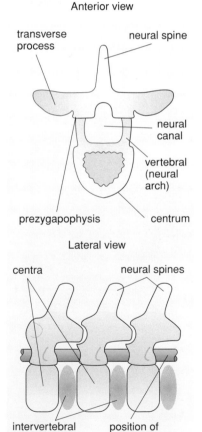

Figure 5.21 A typical vertebra

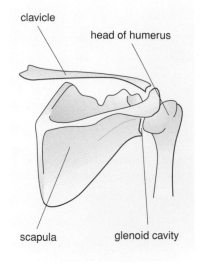

Figure 5.22 The pectoral girdle

Table 5.6 *Vertebrae in the human vertebral column*

Type of vertebra	Number and location	Distinguishing features
cervical	7 neck region	small centrum; large neural canal; short, forked neural spine; vertebrarterial canals in transverse processes
thoracic	12 chest/thorax	long, backward-pointing neural spines; facets for articulation with ribs
lumbar	5 waist, small of back	short, sturdy neural spine and transverse processes; large centrum
sacral	5 lower back, pelvic region	fused to form the sacrum; articulates with pelvis
coccyx	4 form vestigial tail	fused and attached to the posterior part of the sacrum

The **pectoral girdle** is also in two halves, but there is no fusion of bones involved. On each side is a ventral **clavicle** (the collar bone) and a dorsal **scapula** (the shoulder blade). The clavicles articulate with the sternum and each scapula is attached to the ribcage by muscles. The upper arm bones articulate with the pectoral girdle at the glenoid cavity, forming a ball and socket joint.

Both the forelimbs and the hindlimbs conform to the same pentadactyl limb plan as shown in Figure 5.23.

The upper part of each limb consists of a single long bone, the **femur** in the leg and the **humerus** in the arm. These articulate with the limb girdles at their upper ends and with the two bones of the lower part of each limb at the opposite ends. In the leg, the femur articulates with the **tibia** and **fibula** and in the arm, the humerus articulates with the **radius** and the **ulna**. In the arm, a group of eight small bones, called **carpals**, forms the wrist. This articulates with the **metacarpals** and then with the **phalanges**, forming the hand. In the leg, there are seven **tarsals** forming the ankle, articulating with five **metatarsals** and the phalanges forming the foot.

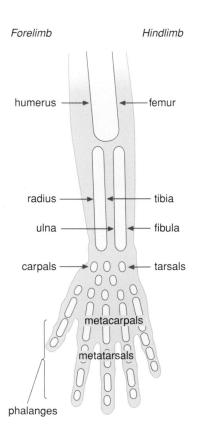

Figure 5.23 The pentadactyl limb

Bone structure

A long bone, such as the humerus or femur, consists of a hollow shaft, called the **diaphysis**, with a head, or **epiphysis,** at each end. The bone is surrounded by a tough, fibrous membrane called the **periosteum**.

The hollow shaft contains bone marrow, which produces many types of blood cells, and the rounded epiphyses articulate with other bones and also form the sites of attachment of tendons holding muscles in place. The diaphysis is composed of compact bone, but the epiphyses are made up of spongy bone with a thin layer of compact bone on the outside. This arrangement of tissue within the bone gives it strength and enables it to withstand compression forces. Compact bone is a calcified connective tissue composed of bone cells embedded in a matrix of collagen fibres and inorganic salts. The matrix consists

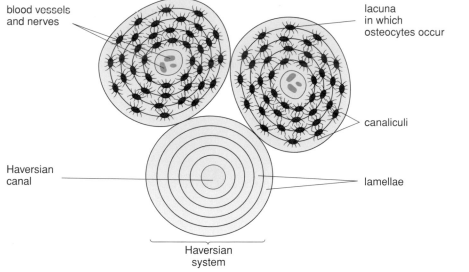

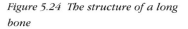

Figure 5.25 Bone tissue

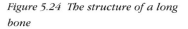

Figure 5.24 The structure of a long bone

of 30 per cent organic material – the **collagen fibres** – and 70 per cent inorganic material. Most of the inorganic component of bone is **hydroxyapatite**, a complex salt containing calcium, phosphate and hydroxyl ions, together with other inorganic ions such as magnesium. The components are arranged in **Haversian systems**, which are orientated parallel to the long axis of the bone and consist of concentric cylinders of lamellae surrounding a central canal, the Haversian canal. The Haversian canal contains blood vessels, nerves and lymphatic vessels. The bone cells, called **osteocytes**, lie in cavities called **lacunae**, from which fine channels, the **canaliculi**, radiate. The canaliculi contain cytoplasm, forming links with other bone cells and with the central Haversian canal.

The blood vessels in the Haversian canals supply the living bone cells with nutrients and oxygen and remove waste substances. Transverse Haversian canals connect the marrow cavity with the longitudinal canals. The **periosteum**, covering the outside of the bone, contains bundles of collagen fibres, referred to as Sharpey-Schafer fibres, which project into the bone and make a firm connection between the periosteum and the bone.

Osteoporosis

The level of calcium in the blood is kept in balance by the action of two hormones, **parathormone** (parathrin) and **calcitonin**. Parathormone is secreted by the parathyroid glands, located close to the thyroid gland, and has the following effects:

- it stimulates the release of calcium from bone if calcium levels in the blood are low
- it promotes the reabsorption of calcium ions from the proximal convoluted tubule of the kidney nephron
- it promotes the absorption of calcium ions from the gut.

All these tend to elevate the level of calcium ions in the blood. Calcitonin, secreted from the thyroid gland, tends to lower the concentration of calcium ions in the blood by promoting the deposition of calcium phosphate in bone.

Parathormone and calcitonin are antagonistic to each other and it is the balance between the two hormones which regulates the concentrations of calcium and phosphate in the body. Oestrogens have been shown to inhibit the action of parathormone, but when oestrogen secretion stops, after the female menopause, the output of parathormone is not inhibited. This results in bone deterioration through loss of calcium and may lead to fractures. This is more common in females than in males, because oestrogen secretion continues in males. Oestrogen treatment in the form of HRT (hormone replacement therapy) helps to redress the situation.

Joints

Joints are formed where bones meet and make movement possible. A variety of joints exists in the mammalian skeleton. These are summarised in Table 5.7.

Table 5.7 *Joints in the mammalian skeleton*

Type of joint and example	General characteristics	Function
immovable/suture e.g. bones of skull, bones of pelvic girdle	formed by thin layers of connective tissue holding bones together	provides protection, strength and support
gliding e.g. between vertebrae, between ribs and thoracic vertebrae	bones separated by pads of cartilage	enables bones to glide over each other
swivel/pivot e.g. atlas and axis		allows shaking of head from side to side
hinge e.g. elbow, knee, finger	synovial joint	allows movement in one plane between two articulating bones
ball and socket e.g. shoulder, hip	synovial joint; ball-shaped end of one bone articulates with cup-shaped cavity of another	allows movement in all planes, including rotation

Hinge and ball and socket joints are **synovial joints**, where the ends of the articulating bones are covered by a smooth layer of cartilage. The bones are held in position by ligaments made of collagen fibres, which form a tough capsule, limiting the movement at the joint and preventing dislocation. The capsule is lined with a synovial membrane, which secretes **synovial fluid** into the cavity of the capsule.

The cartilage reduces friction between the bones and can also act as a shock absorber. The synovial fluid, which is formed from the blood plasma, is a watery liquid containing mucin and phagocytic cells. In addition to lubricating the joint and providing nutrients for the cartilage, it helps to reduce friction between the bones. The synovial fluid does not leak out of the joint because the synovial membrane is waterproof, sealing it off effectively.

Arthritis

Arthritis, or more accurately **osteoarthritis**, is a disorder in which a weight-bearing joint is damaged by wear and tear and other factors. The protective layers of cartilage are worn away and the joint becomes swollen and painful, making movement difficult. Treatment to alleviate the pain and reduce the inflammation may give some relief, but often the joint becomes so damaged that replacement is needed. Replacement of damaged hip joints by an artificial implant is now common, and replacement of other joints such as knees and fingers can be done. The artificial hip joint consists of a metal and plastic structure, which totally replaces the damaged parts. The femur shaft and ball are usually made of titanium and the socket has a polyethylene liner. These components have been chosen for their durability and for their similar properties to the tissues being replaced.

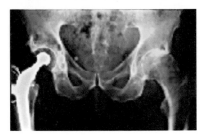

Figure 5.26 Artificial hip joint

Muscle–bone connections

In order to bring about movement at a joint, a skeletal muscle needs at least two points of attachment to the skeleton. It is attached to a non-movable (stationary) part, called the **origin**, and to a freely movable part, called the **insertion**. Muscles are attached to bones by means of tendons or by muscle fibres directly joined to the bone. Tendons are made up of white fibrous connective tissue consisting of bundles of collagen fibres packed tightly together. Alongside the collagen fibres are flattened, oval fibroblasts (the cells which produce the fibres), and the bundles are held together by areolar connective tissue. This arrangement of the bundles of collagen fibres provides the tissue with some flexibility as well as tensile strength

In order for the attachment to be secure, one end of a tendon is continuous with the outer covering of the muscle, whilst the other end is firmly attached to the periosteum surrounding the bone. The **biceps** muscle, situated at the front of the upper arm, has its origin on the scapula, where there are two tendons attaching the muscle to the bone, and its insertion on the radius where there is one tendon. This muscle is antagonistic with the **triceps** muscle behind the upper arm bone, the humerus. Contraction of the biceps muscle causes movement at the elbow joint and the lower part of the arm is raised. At the same time, the triceps muscle is relaxed. When the triceps muscle contracts, the biceps relaxes and the arm is straightened at the elbow. It is important to note that the movement is brought about by contraction and relaxation of the muscles, so the tendons attaching the muscles to the bones should be inelastic.

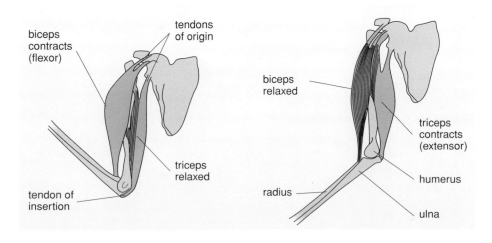

Figure 5.27 Movement at the elbow

Most movements, particularly those at ball and socket joints, are more complex and involve more than one pair of antagonistic muscles, so it is more usual to find groups of muscles working together **synergistically**.

Effect of exercise on muscles

Exercise can have several effects on muscle structure and on the way in which it functions. Basic muscle size appears to be determined genetically, but it has been observed that exercise can increase muscle bulk by up to 60 per cent. With regular exercise, individual muscle fibres increase in diameter and the number of myofibrils within each muscle fibre increases. In addition, the number of muscle fibres in a muscle will increase. It has been observed that the number and size of mitochondria within the muscle tissue increase and those processes occurring in the mitochondria which result in the release of energy take place more rapidly. The ability to generate ATP may be doubled.

Muscle strength is increased if the muscle is used to work against loads greater than it would normally. This can be achieved by making the muscle work harder, increasing the intensity of the exercise, or by making the muscle work for a longer period of time. The exercise has to be carried out regularly in order to maintain the strength of the muscle. If the muscle is not subjected to this exercise on a regular basis, it will revert to its former state.

If exercise results in increase in muscle bulk, then the cross-sectional area of the muscle will increase. It has been estimated that each square centimetre of cross-sectional area can produce between 10 and 20 newtons of measured force, so the bigger the muscle the greater the measured force produced.

Reproduction

The production of new individuals of the same species is a fundamental characteristic of living organisms. Reproduction allows for the replacement of individuals that die and ensures the continuity of the species. If conditions are favourable, it can also result in an increase in numbers. Genetic information from the individuals of one generation, the **parental generation**, is passed on to the next generation, the **offspring**, ensuring that the characteristic features of a species are perpetuated.

Reproduction may be asexual or sexual. **Asexual reproduction** usually involves a single individual and no gamete formation occurs. The offspring inherit identical genetical information from the parent and may be referred to as clones. New individuals are formed from mitotic divisions and the only genetic variation possible arises as a result of random mutation. Few animal species reproduce naturally in this way, although both animals and plants have been successfully cloned using artificial techniques. **Sexual reproduction** involves the formation and fusion of **gametes** from two individuals of the same species. The process of gamete formation includes meiotic division, halving the chromosome number. The resulting offspring are likely to show genetic variation, due to the events of meiosis and the random fusion of gametes at fertilisation.

Asexual reproduction

Fission

The simplest type of asexual reproduction, referred to as **fission**, can be observed in unicellular organisms, where division of the parent cell results in the production of identical daughter cells. The trigger for this type of reproduction is thought to be the nucleus to cytoplasm ratio, so that it occurs when the organism has reached a certain size. In eukaryotes, the parent cell DNA undergoes replication: mitotic nuclear division occurs, followed by division of the cytoplasm (cytokinesis). In **binary fission**, two genetically identical daughter cells result. This type of division can be seen in members of the Protoctista (*Amoeba, Pleurococcus, Paramecium*).

In prokaryotes, binary fission is preceded by replication of the DNA. It has been observed in many bacteria that the DNA is held in position by a mesosome whilst this replication is occurring. After separation of the DNA molecules, a new cross wall is formed, resulting in two daughter cells. When conditions for growth are favourable, this type of division can take place very rapidly.

In the unicellular green alga, *Chlorella*, the parent cell undergoes two mitotic divisions and four daughter cells are produced In some protoctistans, such as the malarial parasite, *Plasmodium*, **multiple fission** occurs. Repeated divisions of the parent nucleus produce very large numbers of daughter cells. This type of fission is an adaptation by the parasite to the problems associated

Amoeba

Amoeba rounds off

Nucleus divides mitotically

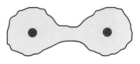

Daughter nuclei migrate to opposite ends

Separation of cytoplasm

Two daughter cells formed.

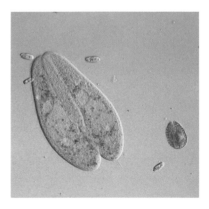

Figure 6.1 Binary fission in Amoeba *(top) and* Paramecium *(bottom)*

with its transfer from primary to secondary host. On entering the primary host, the sporozoites of the parasite invade the liver and feed on the contents of the cells. Each sporozoite can divide to form a thousand daughter cells, called merozoites, which are released into the blood of the primary host. Each merozoite can enter and feed on a red blood cell, producing more merozoites. The greater the number of merozoites in the blood of the infected primary host, the more likely it is that some will be taken up and infect the secondary host, the female mosquito, whilst it is feeding.

Spore formation

Spore formation occurs in bacteria, fungi and green plants. **Spores** are tiny reproductive structures, consisting of one or more nuclei and a small quantity of cytoplasm. It is worth noting that spore formation in bacteria differs from that of the other groups in that one thick-walled resistant spore is usually formed inside the parent cell. The function of this type of spore is to enable the organism to survive adverse conditions. The spore can remain dormant for a long time and will germinate in favourable conditions to release one or two cells.

The spores of many fungi are produced in special structures called **sporangia** (singular: **sporangium**). *Mucor*, a member of the phylum Zygomycota and commonly known as the pin mould fungus, grows on damp bread. The spores develop in a sporangium which forms at the tip of an aerial hypha called a sporangiophore. The tip of the **sporangiophore** swells up and becomes filled with multinucleate cytoplasm, which becomes separated from the rest of the mycelium by the growth of a cross wall, the **columella**. The contents of the sporangium divide up to form the spores (called **sporangiospores**), each containing several nuclei and a small amount of cytoplasm surrounded by a thin wall. The spores, which are small and light, are dispersed by air currents or insects when the sporangial wall splits. In favourable conditions, each spore can grow into a new mycelium if it lands on a suitable food source. Spore formation occurs when there is a plentiful food supply and enables the organism to colonise new food sources rapidly. Inevitably, there is great wastage of spores as the majority will fail to land in a suitable environment.

As you go through the first part of this chapter, list the ways in which spores differ from seeds.

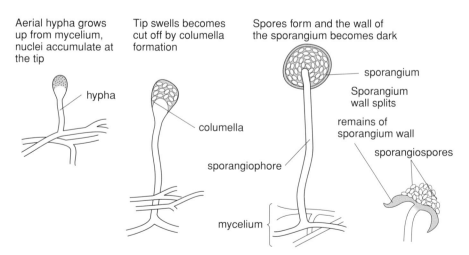

Figure 6.2 Mucor showing spore formation and spore dispersal

In mosses, ferns and flowering plants, a spore-producing stage, the **sporophyte**, is present in the life cycle. The fern *Dryopteris* bears sporangia on the underside of the fronds. The spores are produced by meiosis and are haploid. In suitable conditions, the spores germinate to produce a gamete-producing stage, the **gametophyte**. Haploid male and female gametes are produced by mitosis on the gametophyte and fertilisation results in the formation of a diploid zygote, which grows into a new sporophyte stage. This type of life cycle is known as an **alternation of generations**, as the diploid sporophyte alternates with the haploid gametophyte.

In flowering plants, the gametophyte stage is very reduced and contained within the sporophyte generation. Within the flowers **microspores**, known as **pollen grains**, are produced in the pollen sacs of anthers and **megaspores**, known as **embryo sacs**, are produced in the ovules of carpels.

The spores of ferns and mosses and the microspores of flowering plants are small, light structures which are easily dispersed, thus contributing to the spread of the organisms and increasing the chances of survival.

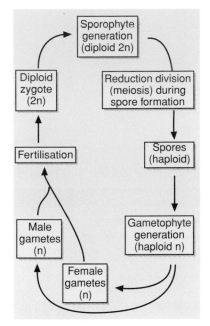

Figure 6.3 Alternation of generations in the plant kingdom

Budding

A form of asexual reproduction in which a new individual develops as an outgrowth of the parent, budding occurs in several groups of organisms. The simplest example of budding is seen in the unicellular yeast, *Saccharomyces*, where a daughter cell is budded off one end of the parent cell. The daughter cell is genetically identical to the parent cell and can become established as an independent individual on separation. More complex examples are seen in *Hydra*, a cnidarian, and in *Bryophyllum*, a succulent house plant.

Figure 6.4 Bryophyllum

Some invertebrate animals are able to regenerate from small fragments. If the anterior end of *Chaetopterus*, an annelid, is pulled by a predator, the body breaks into two pieces between segments 12 and 13. Regeneration of the anterior part of the animal can then occur from what remains. This animal has remarkable powers of regeneration and a complete worm can be regenerated from a single segment.

Vegetative reproduction

Vegetative reproduction, otherwise known as **vegetative propagation**, is a form of asexual reproduction which occurs in green plants. It involves the formation of specialised structures, sometimes referred to as **propagules**, derived from modified roots and stems, which can become detached from the parent plant and grow into independent plants. The offspring produced in this manner are again genetically identical to the parent plant. In some cases, the development of the propagule involves the accumulation of a food store resulting from photosynthesis by the parent plant. This food store enables rapid growth following a period of unfavourable conditions such as drought or cold temperatures. Such propagules are typical of many herbaceous perennial plants and are referred to as **perennating organs**. Table 6.1 summarises vegetative propagation in flowering plants.

Table 6.1 *Vegetative propagation in flowering plants*

Perennating organ	Derivation	Description
bulb e.g. tulip, daffodil, shallot propagation and perennation	modified shoot with a food store in the surrounding fleshy, swollen leaf bases	short conical stem surrounded by swollen leaf bases; adventitious roots; contains one or more buds; if more than one bud grows then new bulbs produced
corm e.g. crocus, gladiolus propagation and perennation	modified stem with a food store	short, vertical underground stem; adventitious roots; one or more buds; axillary buds may form new plants
rhizome e.g. mint, iris, couch grass propagation and perennation	modified stem; short and swollen with stored food in iris, long and thin in mint and couch grass	horizontal underground stem; bears leaves, buds and adventitious roots; axillary buds can give rise to new rhizomes
stolon e.g. blackberry propagation only	modified stem; no food store so not a perennating organ	horizontal, creeping stem on surface of ground; adventitious roots develop at nodes which touch ground; new plant grows from axillary bud
runner e.g. strawberry, creeping buttercup propagation only	modified stem similar to stolon; develops from axillary bud	grows more rapidly than stolon; runner bears axillary buds which develop adventitious roots; new plants formed; runner decays
stem tuber e.g. potato propagation and perennation	modified stem swollen with food store	produced at tips of thin underground stems (rhizomes); axillary buds on tuber can give rise to new plants in next growing season
root tuber e.g. dahlia propagation and perennation	modified root swollen with food store	food stored in swollen adventitious roots; new plants develop from growth of axillary buds at base of old stem
swollen tap root e.g. carrot, turnip characteristic of biennial plants	modified main root, swollen with food store	food store formed during first growing season; used to produce flowers and seeds during second growing season

Many of the examples of vegetative propagation given in Table 6.1 are used by growers and horticulturalists to produce new plants of a desired variety. This is especially relevant to the production of food crops, where particular varieties have been developed by cross-breeding for high yield and resistance to diseases. Potatoes are grown from their stem tubers, known as 'seed' potatoes. The grower then knows that the crop will have the desired characteristics and that it will become established more quickly than if seed is sown.

Many plant parts, when detached, have the ability to grow into new, complete plants and gardeners make use of this in the **artificial propagation** of plants by budding, cuttings and grafting. Some of these techniques are summarised in Table 6.2.

Table 6.2 *Artificial propagation techniques*

Technique	Description	Use
budding	vegetative buds from the desired variety are inserted on to rootstock	particularly useful for roses which do not breed true if grown from seed; rapid method for producing large numbers of plants when demand is high
soft tip cuttings	non-woody (juvenile) shoots used; stem cut below a node; fast-growing so no need for rooting hormone; susceptible to water loss so mist irrigation used	used in the commercial production of chrysanthemums; now grown so that flowering plants can be produced at any season by controlling the photoperiod
hardwood cuttings	mature shoots about 20 cm long cut just below a node; inserted into soil; rooting hormone may be used to encourage growth of roots	useful for rapid production of fruit bushes such as blackcurrants; root readily; usually fruit the following year
grafting	selected variety of scion inserted into suitable rootstock; arranged so that there is good contact between the vascular tissues of both parts	used to propagate fruit trees, particularly apples, where cuttings are not successful; rootstock can be chosen so that size of plant regulated; more difficult and time-consuming than other methods so used only if other methods not suitable

Artificial cloning

Artificial cloning of plants and animals has arisen from the development of techniques used to demonstrate that the nuclei of mature cells contain all the necessary genetic information to code for an entire organism. In plants, **tissue culture** is widely used for the rapid propagation of many desired varieties. Cambium tissue from meristematic regions is cultured on media containing suitable nutrients and appropriate growth substances. Very large numbers of genetically identical plants can be produced using these techniques. Commercial crop propagation by this method uses small portions of shoot meristems and only differs from the technique of using cuttings in that very small parts are used and the conditions in which growth takes place are aseptic and carefully controlled. The technique is referred to as **micropropagation**.

The cloning of animals has been achieved using cells from embryos, but the techniques are not used on the same scale as the cloning of plants by micropropagation. The process of **embryo transfer** used in the selective breeding of cattle involves the extraction of embryos from a suitable donor cow. The cow is made to release a large number of secondary oocytes at ovulation. It is then mated with the desired bull, or artificially inseminated, and the embryos are allowed to develop for 6 to 8 days. The embryos are then removed and at this stage they can be examined and screened for abnormalities before transplanting into surrogate cows to complete their development. In order to obtain clones, it is possible to split the embryo before transplanting it into the surrogate mother. Half the embryo is then placed back into the original fertilised egg and half into an unfertilised egg which has had its secondary oocyte removed. Both embryos can be transplanted into surrogate mothers to continue their development. These two embryos will develop into calves which are genetically identical, in other words clones.

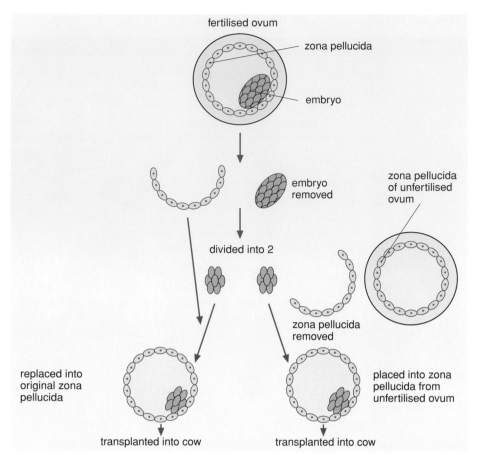

Figure 6.5 Cloning in the selective breeding of cattle

There has been much discussion about the ethics of cloning vertebrate organisms and it is likely that the debate will continue. There are obvious advantages in the use of such techniques in the breeding of domestic animals, but any possibility of cloning human beings raises serious ethical questions.

Sexual reproduction

Sexual reproduction involves the fusion of nuclei with the **haploid** (n) number of chromosomes to form a **diploid zygote** (2n). These haploid nuclei are usually contained within special cells called **gametes**. The diploid zygote then undergoes mitotic divisions and grows into a new individual which, when mature, will be capable of producing gametes. In order to prevent chromosome doubling, meiosis occurs at some stage in the life cycle, reducing the chromosome number from diploid to haploid. A combination of the events which take place during prophase I of meiosis and the random nature of fertilisation leads to genetic variation in the offspring and ensures that each new individual is unique.

During meiosis the following opportunities for the reshuffling of genetic material occur:
- during prophase I, there may be exchange of portions of chromatids between homologous chromosomes (crossing-over), resulting in new combinations of alleles and the formation of new linkage groups

- the orientation of the maternal and paternal chromosomes on the spindle at metaphase I is random, leading to new combinations of maternal and paternal alleles on separation at anaphase I
- the orientation of the chromosomes on the spindle at metaphase II is also random so that the maternal and paternal chromosomes are distributed randomly in the daughter nuclei.

Each gamete nucleus contains one set of chromosomes, so there is only one allele for each gene locus. As all four daughter cells will be different, random fusion of the gametes, each with a unique set of chromosomes, will result in the offspring being different from the parents.

We usually think of gametes as being male or female; the male gamete being small and motile whereas the female gamete is non-motile and larger with more cytoplasm. This distinction is not always evident and in some primitive groups of protoctistans, such as the algae, gametes may be identical (**isogamy**), vary in size (**anisogamy**) or show clear separation into a small motile male and a large non-motile female (**oogamy**). Some organisms produce both male and female gametes, a condition known as **hermaphroditism**, but others are **unisexual**, producing gametes of one type only. The majority of angiosperm flowers and many animal groups are hermaphrodite and some of these groups show interesting adaptations which prevent self-fertilisation. Protandry, where male gametes mature first, and protogyny, in which female gametes mature before the male gametes, are common.

Sexual reproduction in flowering plants

As discussed earlier in this chapter, flowering plant life cycles show an alternation of generations. There is a spore-producing stage, called the **sporophyte generation**, and a gamete-producing stage, called the **gametophyte generation**. In order to gain a better understanding of how these stages fit into the life cycle of flowering plants, it is relevant to consider the life cycles of other plant groups, such as mosses and ferns. In both these groups, the two stages are quite distinct and may exist independently of each other. In mosses, the gametophyte is the dominant generation, with the sporophyte being dependent on it for water and nutrients. In ferns, the situation is reversed, with a dominant, persistent sporophyte generation and a much reduced gametophyte. These life cycles are summarised in Figure 6.6. It is worth noting that meiosis occurs prior to the formation of spores, so that the gametophyte generation is always haploid and the gametes are produced by mitosis. On fusion of the gametes, a diploid zygote is formed and this grows into a diploid sporophyte. In flowering plants, the sporophyte generation is the dominant generation and the gametophyte stages are very much reduced when compared to mosses and the ferns.

In mosses and ferns, only one type of spore is produced in the sporangia of the sporophyte generation, but in flowering plants two types of spores are formed. Microspores, known as **pollen grains**, are produced in microsporangia (the pollen sacs of the anthers) and megaspores, which give rise to the female gametophyte, develop in megasporangia. This difference in

REPRODUCTION

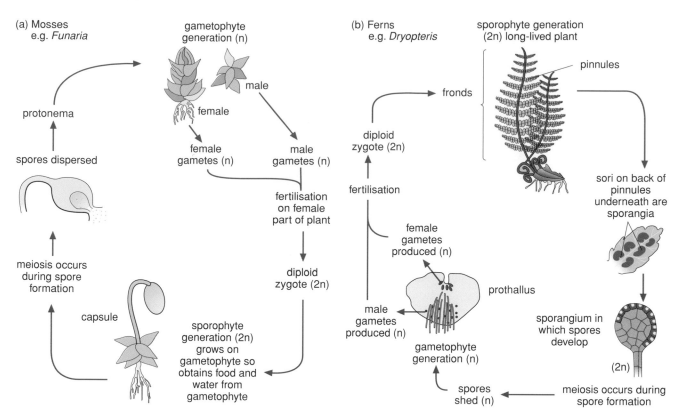

(a) Mosses e.g. *Funaria*

gametophyte generation (n)

male

female

protonema

female gametes (n)

male gametes (n)

spores dispersed

fertilisation on female part of plant

meiosis occurs during spore formation

diploid zygote (2n)

capsule

sporophyte generation (2n) grows on gametophyte so obtains food and water from gametophyte

(b) Ferns e.g. *Dryopteris*

sporophyte generation (2n) long-lived plant

pinnules

fronds

diploid zygote (2n)

fertilisation

female gametes produced (n)

sori on back of pinnules underneath are sporangia

male gametes produced (n)

prothallus

gametophyte generation (n)

sporangium in which spores develop

(2n)

spores shed (n)

meiosis occurs during spore formation

Figure 6.6 Alternation of generations in mosses and ferns

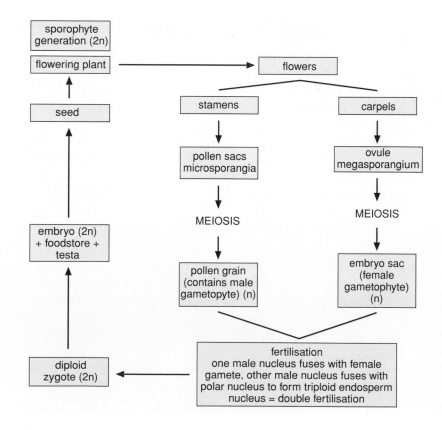

sporophyte generation (2n)

flowering plant → flowers

seed

stamens

carpels

pollen sacs microsporangia

ovule megasporangium

MEIOSIS

MEIOSIS

embryo (2n) + foodstore + testa

pollen grain (contains male gametopyte) (n)

embryo sac (female gametophyte) (n)

diploid zygote (2n)

fertilisation
one male nucleus fuses with female gamete, other male nucleus fuses with polar nucleus to form triploid endosperm nucleus = double fertilisation

Figure 6.7 Alternation of generations in a flowering plant life cycle

size is significant in that the female spores are associated with the accumulation of a food reserve enabling survival and establishment of the embryo after fertilisation. It is possible to trace the evolution of this difference in size of the spores by studying the life cycles of other plant groups such as club mosses (Lycopodophyta) and gymnosperms (Coniferophyta).

Floral structure

The reproductive organs of flowering plants are borne in **flowers**, which are often hermaphrodite, possessing both male and female structures. The male parts are the **stamens**, forming the **androecium**, and the female parts are the **carpels**, forming the **gynaecium**. All the flower parts arise from the enlarged apex of the flower stalk, a region known as the **receptacle**. In addition, there are may be accessory structures such as **sepals**, **petals** and **nectaries** arranged in whorls, or circles, around the reproductive organs. These accessory structures may show wide varieties of form and are often associated with the way in which pollination is achieved. Each stamen is made up of a stalk, called the **filament**, supporting the lobed **anthers** in which there are usually four **pollen sacs**. Each carpel consists of a receptive **stigma** connected to an **ovary** by the **style**. In the ovary, one or more **ovules** develop.

Flowering plants are divided into two major subgroups, Monocotyledones and Dicotyledones. There are differences in the internal arrangement of tissues, but members of the two groups can generally be distinguished from each other by their leaves and flowers. Monocotyledonous plants usually have long, thin leaves with parallel veins, whereas dicotyledonous plants show a wide range of leaf forms, both simple and compound, and the venation is described as reticulate as it forms a dense network. The flower parts in monocotyledons are arranged in threes or sixes and there is often no distinction between the calyx and the corolla, the petals and sepals being referred to as the **perianth segments**. In dicotyledons, the flower parts are often in fours or fives, or multiples of four and five, and there is usually a clear distinction between the calyx and the corolla. In the Gramineae (grasses), a large monocotyledonous family, there are no petals or sepals; the accessory structures consist of small structures called bracts.

Development of pollen and ovules

In the early stages of their development, each pollen sac contains a central mass of microspore mother cells surrounded by a nutritive layer called the **tapetum**. The microspore mother cells undergo meiosis to produce tetrads of haploid cells, each of which develops into a pollen grain, or microspore. The haploid nucleus divides by mitosis to produce a generative nucleus and a pollen tube nucleus. The generative nucleus represents the male gametophyte generation and will undergo a further mitotic division to produce two nuclei which function as male gametes. The pollen grains secrete a thin inner wall, called the **intine**, and a thick outer wall, the **exine**. In wind-pollinated species of flowering plants, the exine of the pollen grains is smooth, but in insect-pollinated species it is often sculptured or pitted.

As the pollen grains mature, the cells of the nutritive layer surrounding each pollen sac shrink and break down and fibrous layers develop in the anther

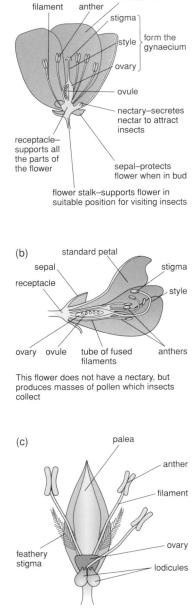

(a) stamen form the androecium — filament — anther — petal–coloured, large to attract insects to flowers — stigma — style — form the gynaecium — ovary — ovule — nectary–secretes nectar to attract insects — receptacle–supports all the parts of the flower — sepal–protects flower when in bud — flower stalk–supports flower in suitable position for visiting insects

(b) standard petal — sepal — stigma — receptacle — style — ovary — ovule — tube of fused filaments — anthers

This flower does not have a nectary, but produces masses of pollen which insects collect

(c) palea — anther — filament — ovary — lodicules — feathery stigma

The palea and lodicules are bracts. The lemma, another bract, has been removed. They are green.

Figure 6.8 (a) Generalised structure of a dicotyledonous flower (b) Flower structure in the family Papilionaceae (c) Flower structure in the family Gramineae

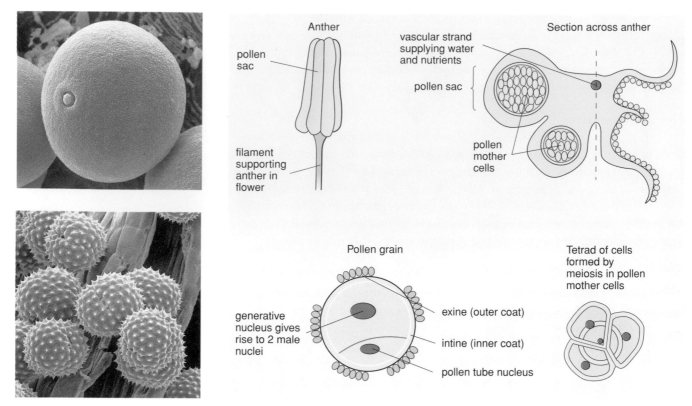

(Photographs) Pollen grains from (top) wind-pollinated and (bottom) insect-pollinated flowers

Figure 6.9 (Diagram) Development of pollen grains

wall. Drying of the anther sets up tensions in the wall, which eventually splits along a longitudinal line of weakness, the two edges curl away and the mass of mature pollen grains is exposed.

Inside the ovary of the carpel, each ovule begins as a small outgrowth from the placenta. This tiny structure is called the **nucellus** and at its apex a megaspore mother cell undergoes meiosis, producing four haploid megaspores. Normally, only one of these will continue to develop by undergoing three successive mitotic divisions, resulting in the formation of an embryo sac containing eight haploid nuclei. The embryo sac represents the female gametophyte generation in the life cycle and is completely enclosed and nourished by the sporophyte generation. As the nucellus gets bigger, it becomes surrounded by two layers of cells, called the **integuments**, which grow from the base of the ovule. In a mature ovule, these layers do not completely surround the nucellus, but a small opening, the **micropyle**, is left.

As the ovule matures, each of the eight nuclei becomes surrounded by some cytoplasm and they are arranged in a definite pattern in the embryo sac. The three nuclei situated at the micropylar end are referred to as the **egg apparatus**. The female gamete, or **egg cell**, is in the centre with a **synergid** on either side. At the opposite end of the embryo sac is another group of three cells referred to as the **antipodal cells**. The remaining two nuclei, called the **polar nuclei**, are found in the centre, where they may remain as separate nuclei or fuse to form a central diploid nucleus. Before pollination and fertilisation, each ovule consists of the nucellus, containing an embryo sac, surrounded by two integuments.

Pollination and fertilisation

Before fertilisation can occur, mature pollen grains containing the male gametes must be transferred to the receptive stigma in a process referred to as pollination. In some species, **self-pollination** occurs. Pollen from the anthers is transferred to the stigma of the same flower, or another flower on the same plant. In other species, **cross-pollination** is achieved, where pollen from the anthers of one flower is transferred to the stigma of a flower on another plant of the same species.

Pollination is usually achieved by wind or insects transferring the pollen from the anthers to the stigmas. Many flowering plant families, such as the Gramineae (grasses) and most trees, are **wind-pollinated**. This mechanism necessitates the production of vast quantities of light, smooth pollen to maximise the chances of some landing on the mature stigmas of the flowers. **Insect pollination** involves the insect as a vector and increases the chances of pollen reaching the stigmas. Insect-pollinated flowers are adapted to this mechanism in that they are coloured and scented to attract the insects, they produce nectar and/or pollen as food for the insects and there are often structural modifications which ensure that pollination is achieved. Table 6.3 summarises the major differences between wind-pollinated and insect-pollinated flowers.

Table 6.3 *The differences between wind-pollinated and insect-pollinated flowers*

Feature	Wind-pollinated flowers	Insect-pollinated flowers
position of flowers	above leaves (grasses) or produced before leaves appear (many trees such as hazel, willow)	often, though not always, above leaves; either solitary and large or smaller and in clusters so conspicuous
petals	small, inconspicuous, sometimes absent (grasses); if present, not brightly coloured	large, brightly coloured, conspicuous; attractive to insects
nectaries	absent	present; insects feed on nectar
scent	not scented	often scented; attracts insects
stamens	hanging outside flower (pendulous)	enclosed within flower
anthers	move freely (versatile) so that pollen is easily dispersed	fixed to filaments; positioned so that they come into contact with visiting insect
pollen	produced in large quantities; light, smooth pollen grains	less produced; pollen grains larger, sculptured walls to aid attachment to insects and to stigma
stigma	large, often branched, often feathery, hanging outside flower to trap pollen	small, enclosed within flower; positioned so that it comes into contact with visiting insect

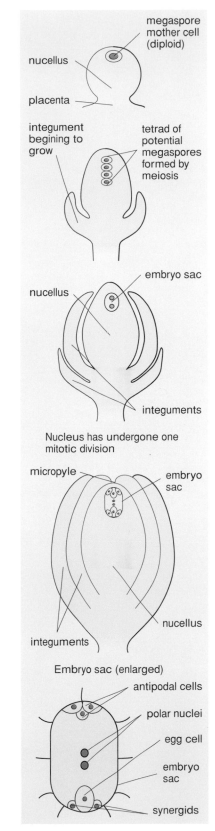

Figure 6.10 Development of embryo sac

Following successful pollination, the epidermal cells of the stigma secrete a solution of sucrose, which stimulates the germination of the pollen grain. A **pollen tube** grows out through one of the pores in the wall of the pollen grain and rapidly penetrates the tissue of the style. The growth of the pollen tube is controlled by the **tube nucleus**, which is located at the tip of the tube, and involves the secretion of digestive enzymes, allowing the penetration of the tissues. The enzymes soften the cutin of the stigma and the middle lamella of the cell walls. Pollen tubes also produce auxin which is involved in the initiation of fruit development. Pollen tubes are positively hydrotropic (growing towards water) and negatively aerotropic (growing away from oxygen). As the pollen tube approaches the ovule, it becomes positively chemotropic to a substance produced by the micropyle and so grows in that direction.

The generative nucleus in the pollen grain undergoes mitosis, forming two **male nuclei**. This division may occur before the mature pollen is shed from the anthers or it may occur during the growth of the pollen tube. The tip of the pollen tube enters the ovule through the micropyle and comes into contact with the embryo sac near the site of the synergids. The male nuclei are released through a pore which develops in the tip of the pollen tube. One of the male nuclei will fuse with the egg nucleus to form a **diploid zygote** and the other male nucleus fuses with the two polar nuclei in the centre of the embryo sac. The diploid zygote gives rise to the **embryo** and the nuclei in the centre fuse to form a triploid nucleus, the **primary endosperm nucleus**, which gives rise to the nutritive tissue known as the **endosperm**. This type of fertilisation is called **double fertilisation** as it involves two fusions. It is also worth noting that the transfer of gametes and the process of fertilisation is adapted to life on land in that no water is needed. In the less adapted groups of plants, such as the mosses and the ferns, water is needed for the transfer of gametes from the male to the female organs.

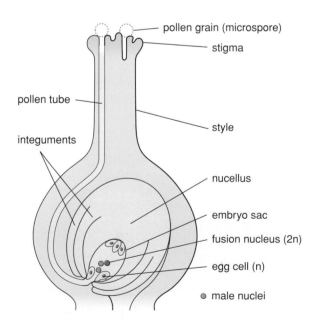

Figure 6.11 A mature carpel showing fertilisation

Mechanisms for ensuring cross-pollination

Self-pollination leads to **self-fertilisation**, where the offspring will only show limited variation due to the recombination of genes from a single parent. Self-fertilisation results in **inbreeding**. If an individual plant, heterozygous at a single locus (**Aa**), is repeatedly selfed, the resulting population becomes homozygous at that locus and two pure-breeding lines, **AA** and **aa**, become established. There is a large number of gene loci in the genome and there will be many ways in which the lines become homozygous, so natural populations of such inbreeding plants will contain different pure lines all breeding true. Self-pollination and self-fertilisation may favour the survival of uncommon or widely-dispersed species, as successful seed production does not depend on wind or insects to disperse the pollen. Common species which show self-pollination are the garden pea (*Pisum sativum*), groundsel (*Senecio vulgaris*) and chickweed (*Cerastium arvense*). In some species, self-pollination is allowed to occur if cross-pollination fails.

Cross-pollination, leading to cross-fertilisation and **outbreeding**, occurs in many species and has the advantage of maintaining heterozygosity and variation, because two different parent plants are involved. Each ovule in a gynaecium must be fertilised by the male nuclei from separate pollen grains. These pollen grains may come from different parent plants, a feature which has the effect of increasing variation still further. A number of different mechanisms have evolved which prevent self-pollination and improve the chances of cross-pollination. Such mechanisms may involve separation of the male and female reproductive organs, dichogamy, self-sterility (self-incompatibility) or heterostyly.

List the advantages and disadvantages of inbreeding and outbreeding.

Although the flowers of most plant species are hermaphrodite, several have separate male and female flowers. **Dioecious** species, such as poplar (*Populus* sp.), willow (*Salix* sp.) and holly (*Ilex* sp.), have male and female flowers on separate plants, so self-pollination is impossible. In **monoecious** species, such as hazel (*Corylus* sp.) and oak (*Quercus* sp.), male and female flowers occur on the same plant, but self-pollination is avoided by a difference in the timing of their development.

In hermaphrodite flowers, self-pollination can be avoided if the male and female organs mature at different times, a condition known as **dichogamy**. In **protandry**, the stamens ripen and the pollen is released from the anthers before the carpels are mature, so the stigmas of the flower are not receptive to pollen at this stage. This mechanism is found in white deadnettle (*Lamium alba*), Canterbury bell (*Campanula medium*), rose-bay willow-herb (*Epilobium angustifolium*) and sage (*Salvia* sp.). In the reverse situation, known as **protogyny**, the carpels mature before the stamens, so the stigma of the flower is receptive to pollen before the anthers have dehisced.

An example of protogyny is seen in the ribwort plantain (*Plantago lanceolata*), where the inflorescence is an erect spike. The lower flowers open first and initially the stigma is receptive to pollen. Later in the same flower, the anthers ripen and release mature pollen. The mature pollen will always be released at a lower level than the receptive stigmas, so it is unlikely that self-pollination will occur.

*Figure 6.12 Protogyny in ribwort plantain (*Plantago lanceolata*)*

Many wind-pollinated flowers, such as members of the Gramineae, are protogynous, but the condition is generally less common than protandry. Among insect-pollinated flowers showing protogyny are wild arum (*Arum maculatum*), bluebell (*Endymion non-scriptus*) and figwort (*Scrophularia nodosa*).

Self-incompatibility, or **self-sterility**, occurs if pollen from the same flower, or another flower on the same plant, lands on the stigma and fails to germinate. Sometimes germination may occur, but the pollen tube grows very slowly and fails to reach the ovules. Proteins are produced on the surfaces of pollen grains and stigmas. Physiological mechanisms enable the stigmas to distinguish between the proteins on pollen from the same plant and pollen from different plants of the same species. When pollen lands on the stigma of the same plant, the proteins are identical and the pollen fails to germinate, so pollen and stigmas are incompatible. Pollen from a different plant of the same species, carrying different surface proteins, will germinate and is said to be compatible. Different forms of these surface proteins are determined by alleles of an incompatibility gene. This recognition system prevents inbreeding and encourages outbreeding.

Heterostyly describes the situation where different kinds of floral morphology exist within a species. One of the best known examples is seen in the primrose (*Primula vulgaris*), where there are differences in the length of the style and the positioning of the anthers. In the thrum-eyed flower, the style is short, placing the stigma low down in the corolla tube. The anthers are situated high up in the corolla tube, above the stigma. In the pin-eyed type, the anthers are low down the corolla tube, but the style is long and the stigma is above the anthers.

Insects visiting the thrum-eyed flowers have pollen deposited high up on the proboscis as they reach inside the flower for nectar. When a pin-eyed flower is visited, the pollen from the thrum-eyed flower gets brushed against the stigma. Pollen from the pin-eyed flower is deposited about halfway along the proboscis, just in the right position to come into contact with the style of the next thrum-eyed flower visited. However, this mechanism is not particularly effective as when the insect withdraws from the pin-eyed flower, pollen from the anthers can be drawn up on to the stigma. Similarly, pollen from the anther of the thrum-eyed flower can get taken down to the stigma as the insect enters. Additionally, pollen from the anthers of the thrum-eyed flower can just fall on to the stigma. There is incompatibility between the pollen and the stigmas of the same flower, so self-fertilisation is prevented. Investigation of the pollination mechanism found in the primrose has shown that the development of the pin and thrum flowers is controlled by two linked genes determining style length and anther position. These two genes also determine the form of the stigma, pollen grain size and the production of the surface proteins involved with the incompatibility reaction.

Work out why pollen from plant A is needed to pollinate plant B when plant A has alleles S_1 and S_2 at the incompatibility locus and plant B has alleles S_3 and S_4.

Make drawings to show the position of the anthers and stigmas in pin-eyed and thrum-eyed flowers to help you work out what happens at pollination.

Seeds and germination

After fertilisation has occurred, the anthers and filaments begin to shrivel and the petals of the flower fall off. The fertilised ovule develops into a **seed** and the ovary develops into a **fruit**. The diploid zygote undergoes mitotic divisions and develops into a multicellular embryo in which can be distinguished

- the **plumule**, the first shoot consisting of a stem and a terminal bud surrounded by the first pair of foliage leaves
- the **radicle**, the first root
- one or two **cotyledons**, known as seed leaves, which are much simpler in structure than the foliage leaves. The embryos of monocotyledonous plants have one cotyledon and those of dicotyledonous plants have two cotyledons.

Within the **endosperm**, large numbers of triploid nuclei are formed, separated from one another by thin cell walls. In some seeds, this tissue forms the food store for the developing embryo, but in others food storage tissue develops in the cotyledons which become large and fleshy and the endosperm tissue disappears. In some seeds, food is stored in both the cotyledons and the endosperm. As the embryo grows, the embryo sac gets bigger and the nucellus breaks down. Materials from the breakdown of the nucellus are used in the growth of the embryo, together with food materials derived from the photosynthesis of the parent plant.

As the seed gets bigger, the integuments form the **testa**, or seed coat, with the micropyle persisting as a tiny pore through which water enters when germination occurs. The testa is tough and protects the seed during its period of dormancy before germination. In the later stages of development, the water content is reduced and metabolic activity is slowed down. Most plant tissues contain about 90 per cent by mass of water, but a mature seed only contains between 15 per cent and 10 per cent.

As the seeds develop, the ovary enlarges and forms the fruit. The ovary wall becomes the **pericarp** which protects the seeds. Changes may occur in the nature of the pericarp and the underlying tissues, so that the fruit becomes either juicy or dry. These changes are linked with the way in which the seeds are dispersed. In the Papilionaceae, the fruits are pods, which become dry when mature and split, releasing the seeds.

Seed dormancy

Some seeds can germinate immediately after they have been shed from the parent plant, provided that they are given the necessary conditions, such as sufficient water, an appropriate temperature and oxygen. Many seeds need an **after-ripening** period before they will germinate. Some seeds need to be left in a dry state for a period of time and many require exposure to a period of low temperature before germination will occur. Light, temperature or growth inhibitors may be involved in seed dormancy. The effects of these factors are summarised in Table 6.4.

Although the factors listed in Table 6.4 are known to affect dormancy and germination, it is not always clear exactly how the mechanisms work and it is probable that a number of factors interact at different stages. It is apparent

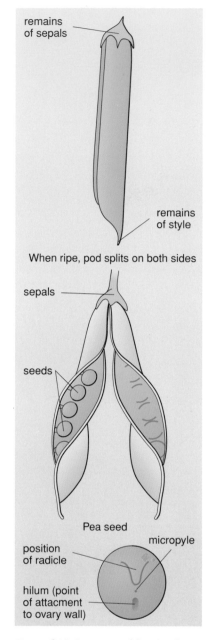

Figure 6.13 Structure of fruit and seed in Papilionaceae

Table 6.4 *Factors affecting seed dormancy*

Factor	Effect on seed dormancy and germination
growth inhibitors	many dormant fruits and seeds contain high levels of abscisic acid; dormancy is broken as levels fall due to soaking or increase in a growth promoter, such as gibberellin
light	germination of some seeds is inhibited by light, e.g. members of family Liliaceae , *Nigella, Phacelia*; in others, light promotes germination, e.g. plants of open areas such as willow herb (*Epilobium*) and foxglove (*Digitalis*), and lettuce varieties. Some seeds are photoperiodic. The detection of the light stimulus involves phytochrome
temperature	many seeds require a cold stimulus after taking up water (known as stratification) before germination will occur; biochemical changes occur, associated with a decrease in abscisic acid and an increase in gibberellins, together with an increase in enzyme activity

that seed dormancy is a survival mechanism and prevents germination occurring at a time which would be unfavourable for the development of the new plant.

Germination

In order for germination to occur, seeds need water, a suitable temperature and oxygen. Seeds take up water through the micropyle in a process called **imbibition**. This is a physical process and occurs because water is adsorbed by colloidal substances within the seed, such as proteins, starch and cell wall materials. As the water is taken up, these materials in the seed swell and cause the testa to rupture, allowing the emergence of the radicle and plumule. Water can pass from cell to cell by osmosis and activates hydrolytic enzyme reactions, which result in the breakdown of the food reserves in the seed. These compounds provide energy and materials to be used for the growth of the embryo.

Germination in cereal grains, such as barley, has been studied in detail and shows the interaction between the imbibition of water and the production of gibberellin in the breaking of dormancy. Cereal grains are one-seeded fruits in which the testa and pericarp are fused. Just below the seed coat is the **aleurone layer**, which contains protein. After the imbibition of water by the seed, the embryo produces gibberellin which diffuses to the aleurone layer where it stimulates enzyme synthesis. The enzymes catalyse the hydrolysis of food reserves in the endosperm of the seed. In cereal grains which have a starchy endosperm, the starch is hydrolysed to maltose by α-amylase and the maltose is hydrolysed to glucose by maltase. The glucose diffuses to the embryo, where it is used to release energy or provide the materials for the synthesis of new cell structures.

Each type of seed germinates within a characteristic temperature range related to the environment in which the plant normally grows. Seeds of plants growing in temperate regions will normally germinate in lower temperatures

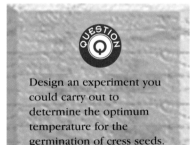

Design an experiment you could carry out to determine the optimum temperature for the germination of cress seeds.

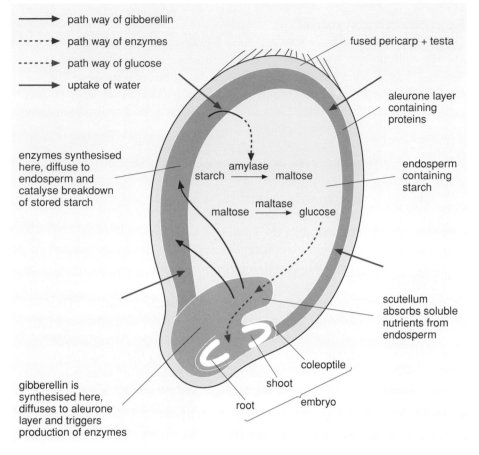

path way of gibberellin
path way of enzymes
path way of glucose
uptake of water

fused pericarp + testa

aleurone layer
containing
proteins

enzymes synthesised
here, diffuse to
endosperm and
catalyse breakdown
of stored starch

amylase
starch → maltose

maltose
maltase
maltose → glucose

endosperm
containing
starch

scutellum
absorbs soluble
nutrients from
endosperm

coleoptile

shoot

root   embryo

gibberellin is
synthesised here,
diffuses to aleurone
layer and triggers
production of enzymes

Figure 6.14 Breaking of dormancy in a cereal grain (barley)

than those of tropical plants. Temperature affects the rate of enzyme-controlled reactions, so very high temperatures will denature enzymes, causing the death of the embryos. Cold temperatures will slow down the process of germination.

Oxygen is required for the process of aerobic respiration, which releases energy for growth. Some anaerobic respiration may occur, but this does not release as much energy and the waste products formed could inhibit germination.

At the onset of germination, the growth of the embryo is rapid. Mitotic divisions result in an increase in the number of cells, which enlarge and become differentiated into the different tissues. The rupture of the testa precedes the emergence of the radicle, which is positively geotropic and grows downwards, anchoring the embryo. Root hairs develop and increase the area available for the uptake of water as well as increasing the stability of the embryo in the soil. The plumule, which is negatively geotropic, emerges after the radicle and grows upwards. As soon as the first foliage leaves appear, photosynthesis can occur and the embryo becomes established as an independent plant able to make its own food.

Reproduction in humans

Reproductive systems

The reproductive systems in the male and female differ in both their structure and their physiology. The female system produces a gamete, the **ovum** (oocyte), which is fertilised by the male gamete, or **spermatozoon**. The resulting zygote develops and implants in the wall of the uterus where it grows and develops until the baby is born after a gestation period of approximately 38 weeks, from fertilisation to delivery.

The **male reproductive system** consists essentially of four major components:

- the **testes**, or male gonads, situated in the scrotum, which are responsible for producing the male gametes, and for secreting male sex hormones
- a system of **ducts**, including the epididymis and ductus deferens (sperm duct), which collect and store spermatozoa from each testis. The ejaculatory ducts converge on the urethra, through which spermatozoa are expelled
- exocrine glands, including the **seminal vesicles** and **prostate gland**, which secrete a nutritive and lubricating fluid, called seminal fluid, with which spermatozoa are mixed. **Semen** consists of spermatozoa, seminal fluid, mucus and cells which are lost from the lining of the duct system
- the **penis**, which contains the urethra and erectile tissue. During sexual arousal, this erectile tissue fills with blood and the penis becomes rigid and increases in both length and diameter. The result is termed an erection which enables the penis to function as a penetrating organ during sexual intercourse.

The functions of the **female reproductive system** are to produce gametes, (the ova), to receive the male gametes, to provide a suitable environment for fertilisation and the development of the fetus and to provide a means of expelling the developed fetus, during the process of parturition, or birth. The internal organs of the female reproductive system consist of:

- the **ovaries**, which are the sites of both the production of ova and the secretion of the hormones oestrogen and progesterone
- a pair of **oviducts** (or Fallopian tubes) which convey the ovum from the ovary to the uterus. Fertilisation of the ovum usually takes place in the oviduct
- the **uterus**, a hollow, pear-shaped, muscular organ. The lining of the uterus, the **endometrium**, undergoes cyclical changes under the influence of the ovarian hormones oestrogen and progesterone. The **cervix** is part of the uterus which projects through the upper part of the vaginal wall
- the **vagina**, a muscular tube which is adapted both for the reception of the penis during sexual intercourse, and for the passage of the baby out of the mother's body during birth.

The structures of the male and female reproductive systems are illustrated in Figure 6.15.

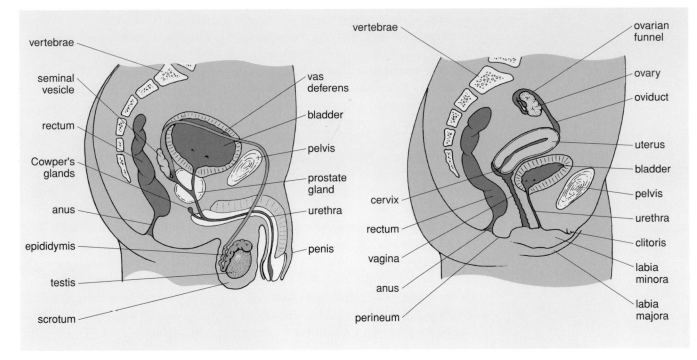

Figure 6.15 The male and female reproductive systems

Gametogenesis and the menstrual cycle

Gametogenesis is the process which results in the formation of gametes. It involves a special form of cell division – meiosis – in which the number of chromosomes is halved. The significance of meiosis in sexual reproduction is described on page 116. Each human testis is packed with numerous coiled **seminiferous tubules**, within which the process of spermatogenesis occurs. **Spermatogenesis** begins at about the time of puberty and normally continues through life. Figure 6.16 shows the major steps in spermatogenesis.

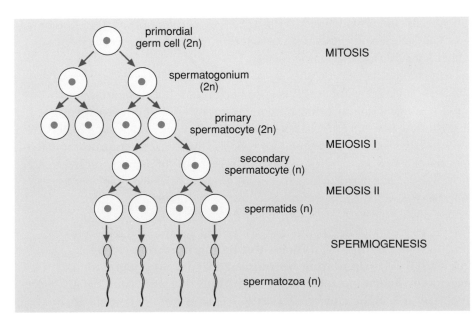

Figure 6.16 Spermatogenesis

Spermatogonia, also known as germ cells, line the seminiferous tubules and divide by mitosis, giving rise to further spermatogonia (known as spermatogonia Type A) and to spermatogonia which will undergo meiosis to form spermatozoa (Type B). Spermatogonia Type B are also known as **primary spermatocytes** and undergo the first meiotic division to form **secondary spermatocytes**. In humans, this first division takes about three weeks to complete. The secondary spermatocytes then rapidly undergo the second meiotic division to form **spermatids**, which undergo a process of development, known as spermiogenesis, to form **spermatozoa**. Spermatogenesis occurs in waves throughout the seminiferous tubules; at any given time some areas are active whilst others are at rest. Studies of spermatogenesis in humans have shown that the entire process takes 74 days. Spermatozoa in the seminiferous tubules are not motile (they only become motile after ejaculation) and are pushed onwards to the epididymis, partly by ciliary activity of cells lining the ducts, and partly by contraction of smooth muscle. The mature human spermatozoon is 55 to 65 μm long and is often described as having a head and a tail. The head, 4 to 5 μm long and 3 μm wide, consists of a nucleus and an acrosome – a membrane-bound structure containing lytic enzymes. The first part of the tail is packed with mitochondria which provide energy for movement of the spermatozoon.

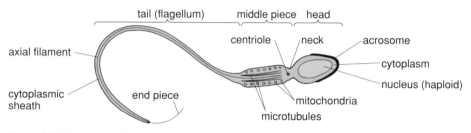

Figure 6.17 Structure of a spermatozoon

During the process of spermatogenesis, the cells are supported by **Sertoli cells** within the seminiferous tubules. Sertoli cells are described as acting as 'nurse cells' and provide mechanical and metabolic support for the developing spermatozoa. Sertoli cells are also phagocytic, and take up excess cytoplasm which is lost during spermatogenesis.

The main function of the testes is spermatogenesis, but they also have an important endocrine role, secreting the male sex hormone **testosterone**. Testosterone is secreted by cells known as Leydig cells, which are situated in the spaces between the seminiferous tubules. Testosterone controls the rate of spermatogenesis and is responsible for a wide range of male characteristics, including aspects of behaviour, increased growth of muscle tissue and changes in the larynx which cause the voice to 'break' at puberty.

The testes are controlled by the anterior pituitary gland which secretes two gonadotrophic hormones, **follicle stimulating hormone** (**FSH**) and **interstitial cell stimulating hormone** (**ICSH**). ICSH is identical in structure to luteinising hormone (LH) which, as described later, has an important role in the menstrual cycle. ICSH stimulates the Leydig cells to secrete testosterone, which has an inhibitory effect on the secretion of FSH and ICSH. In other words, a negative feedback mechanism operates between the anterior pituitary and the testes. FSH acts with testosterone to stimulate the process of spermatogenesis.

Oogenesis is the process by which primordial germ cells, known as oogonia, become mature ova. This process begins during early fetal development, where oogonia divide by mitosis. By the fourth and fifth months, some of these oogonia will have enlarged and have the potential to develop into mature gametes. At this stage they are known as **primary oocytes** and begin the first stage (prophase I) of meiosis. By the seventh month of fetal development, the primary oocytes have become surrounded by a layer of flattened follicular cells, to form **primordial follicles**. The first stage of meiosis then ceases and no further development occurs until after the female reaches puberty. Then, approximately once a month, a few of the primary oocytes resume meiosis and begin to move towards the surface of the ovary. Usually only one follicle reaches full maturity; the others undergo degeneration (atresia). As the follicle develops, it enlarges and fluid begins to accumulate within the follicle. During this stage, the first meiotic division is completed and the oocyte is known as a **secondary oocyte**. At ovulation, the mature follicle (or **Graafian follicle**) ruptures and the secondary oocyte, surrounded by cells from the follicle, is released from the ovary. After the oocyte is released it is usually referred to as an ovum and the second meiotic division will not be completed until the head of a spermatozoon enters during fertilisation.

Figure 6.18 Oogenesis

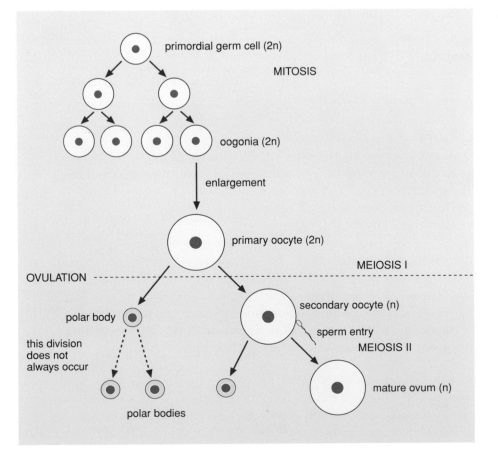

Notice that during oogenesis the meiotic divisions are unequal, that is, the cytoplasm is not distributed equally between the daughter cells. Only one mature ovum is produced from each primary oocyte, plus three polar bodies, which disintegrate. This process ensures that the ovum has a large store of cytoplasm with all of its organelles and nutrients for early development.

After ovulation, the ruptured follicle fills with a blood clot and cells remaining within the follicle enlarge. This forms a temporary endocrine structure, the **corpus luteum**, which grows for 7 or 8 days. During this time, the corpus luteum secretes **progesterone** and **oestrogen**. If fertilisation and implantation do not occur, the corpus luteum degenerates 12 to 14 days after ovulation to form the functionless corpus albicans.

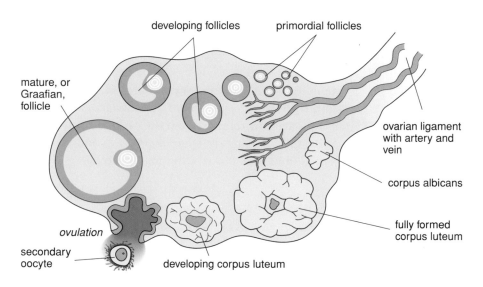

Figure 6.19 Stages of ovarian follicle development

Control of the menstrual cycle

Ovulation is a cyclical process and this is accompanied by corresponding cyclical changes which occur throughout the female reproductive system. These changes depend on two interrelated cycles:
- the ovarian cycle, and
- the uterine (menstrual) cycle.

Both of these cycles are variable, but last approximately 28 days. The menstrual cycle is controlled by the ovarian cycle, via the hormones oestrogen and progesterone. The ovarian cycle, in turn, is controlled by gonadotrophic hormones secreted by the anterior pituitary gland. The gonadotrophic hormones are **follicle stimulating hormone** (**FSH**) and **luteinising hormone** (**LH**) and are secreted in a cyclical pattern.

An initial increase in the blood FSH level stimulates the development of one or more of the primordial follicles and also stimulates follicular cells to secrete oestrogen and small amounts of progesterone. The levels of oestrogen in the blood therefore gradually increase for a few days, then suddenly rise to a peak on about the 12th day of the cycle. About 12 hours afterwards, there is a rise in the levels of both LH and FSH which triggers ovulation. LH also causes the formation of the corpus luteum from the ruptured follicle, which secretes oestrogen and progesterone. If pregnancy does not occur, the lack of FSH and LH causes the corpus luteum to degenerate and the levels of progesterone and oestrogen fall.

The changing concentrations of oestrogen and progesterone during the cycle are responsible for cyclical changes in the uterus. The wall of the uterus has three layers:
- a thin outer layer in contact with the body cavity
- a thick, smooth muscle layer, the **myometrium**
- an inner lining, called the **endometrium**, which provides the environment for development of the fetus.

During the uterine cycle, the endometrium undergoes cyclical changes in structure, which can be divided into three phases:
- the **menstrual phase**, which occurs on days 1 to about 5 of a new cycle. During this phase, the outer layers of the endometrium are lost (menstruation)
- the **proliferative phase** (or follicular phase), which lasts from about day 6 to day 13 or 14 in a 28 day cycle. During this phase, the endometrium becomes thicker as tissue which was lost in menstruation is repaired
- the **secretory phase** (or luteal phase) during which glands in the endometrium start to secrete a thick, glycogen-rich mucus. In this phase, which lasts from ovulation to the end of the cycle, the endometrium is prepared for implantation of the fertilised ovum.

As the blood oestrogen levels rise during the proliferative phase, they produce several changes in the endometrium, including repair and thickening, and an increase in the water content of the endometrium. Increasing blood progesterone levels during the secretory phase are responsible for maintenance of the endometrium, secretion by the endometrial glands and a further increase in the water content. The drop in levels of both oestrogen and progesterone, due to degeneration of the corpus luteum towards the end of the ovarian cycle, is responsible for loss of the outer layers of the endometrium which characterises the menstrual phase.

Feedback and control of the ovarian cycle by gonadotrophins

So far, we have described cyclical changes in the ovary and in the endometrium, and how these changes are, in turn, controlled by the gonadotrophic hormones FSH and LH. The secretion of these gonadotrophins depends on the activity of the **hypothalamus**, which is one reason why female reproductive cycles can be affected by emotional influences, including stress (psychogenic influences).

The hypothalamus controls the secretion of both FSH and LH by means of **gonadotrophin releasing hormone** (GnRH), sometimes referred to as luteinising hormone releasing hormone (LHRH). Both negative and positive feedback mechanisms help to control the secretion of FSH and LH. These mechanisms depend on the secretion of oestrogen and progesterone by the ovaries, and the secretion of GnRH by the hypothalamus. Remember that at the start of the menstrual cycle, the blood level of FSH starts to rise, which in turn stimulates the secretion of oestrogen by follicular cells in the ovary. Oestrogen exerts two types of feedback on the secretion of gonadotrophins: at low levels it inhibits secretion (negative feedback), but at relatively high concentrations it stimulates secretion of gonadotrophins (positive feedback). This effect is responsible for the mid-cycle peak in LH and FSH which triggers ovulation. After ovulation, the level of LH remains relatively high, which stimulates the formation of the corpus luteum. Towards the end of the cycle, however, secretion of LH is inhibited as a result of negative feedback exerted by rising levels of progesterone. As the corpus luteum degenerates, the levels of progesterone fall, and the concentrations of FSH gradually increase again. Oestrogen and progesterone probably exert their effects by affecting the secretion of GnRH by the hypothalamus and changing the sensitivity to GnRH of cells in the anterior pituitary.

Figure 6.20 Female reproductive cycles

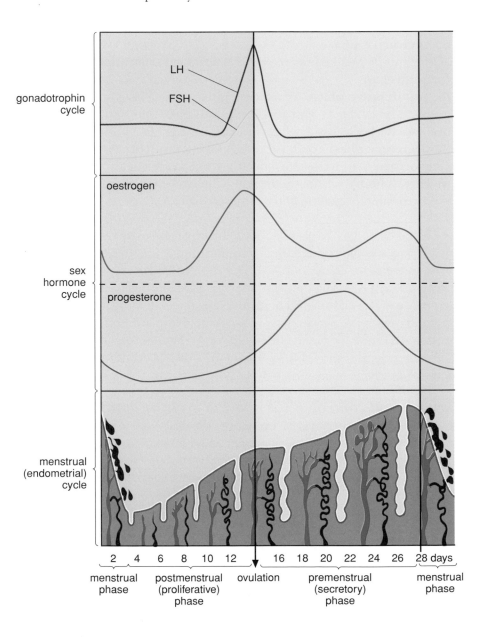

Fertilisation, implantation and early development

Transfer of sperms into the vagina involves erection of the penis and ejaculation of semen. Erection is a parasympathetic nervous reflex initiated by various tactile, visual and psychological stimuli. As a result of dilatation of arteries and arterioles in the penis, spaces in the erectile tissue become distended which compresses the veins. More blood enters the penis than leaves it through the veins and it becomes larger and rigid. Ejaculation of semen is also a reflex involving the same stimuli that initiate erection. Rhythmic contractions of the bulbocavernosus and ischiocavernosus muscles at the base of the penis propel semen into the vagina.

Normal sperms are motile and can move at a rate of about 1.0 mm per minute. Assisted by muscular movements of the uterus, sperms make their way through the cervix and uterus and into the oviducts (Fallopian tubes). Fertilisation occurs most frequently in the outer one third of the oviduct, as shown in Figure 6.21.

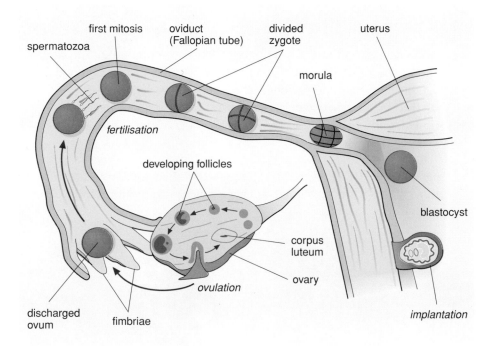

Figure 6.21 Fertilisation and implantation

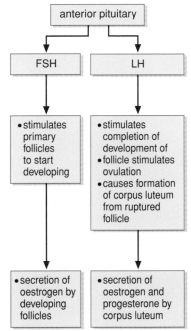

Figure 6.22 Summary of main effects of gonadotrophins (FSH and LH) on the ovaries

Of the 10^8 to 5×10^8 sperms released into the vagina at ejaculation, fewer than 100 reach the oviduct. Only one sperm fertilises the ovum and, as soon as the head of one sperm enters the ovum, complex mechanisms in the ovum are activated to prevent further sperm entry. The 23 chromosomes from the sperm combine with the 23 chromosomes present in the ovum to restore the diploid number of 46 chromosomes.

After ovulation, the ovum lives only for about 24 hours. Sperms may live for up to a few days after entering the female reproductive tract and sexual intercourse from about three days before ovulation occurs, to one day after ovulation, may result in fertilisation.

The fertilised ovum is referred to as a **zygote** and it immediately begins to divide, by mitosis, as it travels down the oviduct. In about three days, a mass of about sixteen cells, known as a **morula**, is formed. The morula enters the uterus and fluid from the uterine cavity enters the morula. The cells rearrange themselves to form a hollow structure, known as a blastocyst. The **blastocyst** begins to implant in the endometrium and, in about ten days from fertilisation, the blastocyst is completely implanted.

The blastocyst consists of an outer layer of cells and an **inner cell mass**.

The outer wall of the blastocyst is referred to as the **trophoblast** and gives rise to structures which support the embryo during development. As the blastocyst develops further, the inner cell mass forms a structure with two cavities, the **yolk sac** and the **amniotic cavity**. Cells within the yolk sac produce blood cells until this function is taken over by the embryonic liver. The amniotic cavity becomes filled with fluid, mainly derived from maternal blood, which physically cushions the developing embryo, maintains a constant temperature and allows free movement of the fetus.

The chorion develops from the trophoblast to form the **placenta**. The surface of the chorion becomes covered with chorionic villi which connect blood vessels of the chorion to the placenta. The placenta has several functions including the transfer of oxygen and carbon dioxide, nutrients, metabolic wastes, antibodies and hormones between the maternal and fetal circulations. Drugs and some infectious organisms can also cross the placenta.

The inner cell mass develops to form the tissues of the baby itself. Early in development, cells within the inner cell mass differentiate to form the three

Figure 6.23 Diagrammatic structure of the placenta

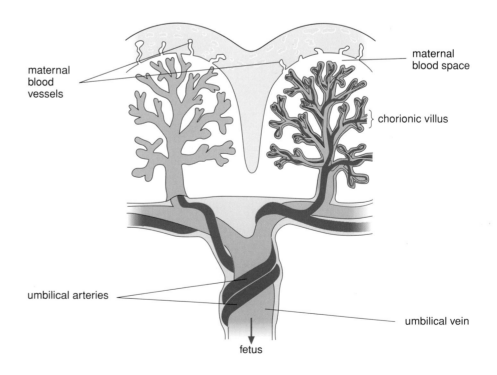

primary germ layers, referred to as the endoderm, mesoderm, and ectoderm. Cells within each of these germ layers continue to divide and differentiate to give rise to all the tissues, organs and systems of the body. As examples, the endoderm gives rise to the lining of the digestive and respiratory tracts; mesoderm forms most of the skeletal muscles and bones, kidneys and gonads; ectoderm forms the epidermis of skin and various components of the nervous system. During the third week of development, the process of **neurulation** occurs, in which the neural tube is formed, from ectoderm, along the dorsal axis of the embryo. The neural tube is the precursor of the nervous system.

The length of pregnancy, about 38 weeks from fertilisation, is divided into three 3-month segments called trimesters. During the first trimester, the term embryo is used to describe the developing individual. Towards the end of the first trimester, the term embryo is replaced by the term fetus from about week 8 until birth. Stages of embryonic and fetal development are illustrated in Figure 6.24.

Birth and lactation

Birth, or **parturition**, is the point of transition between the prenatal and postnatal periods of life. The term l**abour** is used to describe the processes which result in the birth of a baby. Labour is divided into three stages:

- Stage 1: period from the onset of uterine contractions until dilation of the cervix is complete.
- Stage 2: from the time of maximal dilation of the cervix until the baby exits through the vagina.
- Stage 3: process of expulsion of the placenta through the vagina.

The processes which initiate and control parturition are not fully understood, but can be summarised as follows:

- the sensitivity of the uterine muscle to oxytocin increases towards the end of pregnancy
- in sheep and goats, parturition is triggered by the release of corticotrophin releasing hormone from the fetal hypothalamus, which stimulates the secretion of adrenocorticotrophic hormone (ACTH)
- ACTH acts on the fetal adrenal glands and cortisol is secreted which passes from the fetus to the placenta, where it stimulates oestrogen secretion and inhibits progesterone secretion
- as a result, the synthesis of prostaglandin F2α is increased in the placenta and uterus
- this increases the sensitivity of the uterine muscle to oxytocin
- oxytocin from the mother's posterior pituitary gland stimulates contraction of the uterine muscle until the baby is pushed out through the cervix and vagina.

Lactation consists of two processes: milk secretion, and milk ejection. Milk secretion involves the synthesis of milk by secretory cells in the mammary glands. This is stimulated by prolactin, or lactogenic hormone, secreted by the anterior pituitary gland. Milk ejection involves suction by the baby and a contractile mechanism within the mammary glands which helps to express milk. Suckling stimulates the secretion of oxytocin (and prolactin) by the

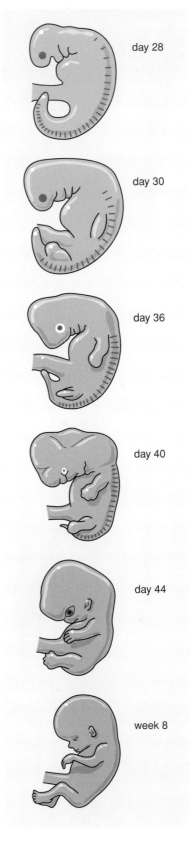

day 28

day 30

day 36

day 40

day 44

week 8

Figure 6.24 Stages of development of the human embryo and fetus

mother's pituitary gland. Oxytocin is then carried in the blood stream to the mammary glands where it stimulates contraction of myoepithelial cells. This propels milk into ducts where it is accessible for the baby to remove by suckling.

The fluid secreted by the mammary glands during the first three days after parturition is termed **colostrum**. This is deep yellow in colour and rich in protein and salts. Milk formed during the first few weeks of lactation is termed transition or intermediate milk. Mature milk is produced at the end of the first month. Milk is a rich source of proteins, fat, calcium, vitamins and other nutrients needed by the developing infant. It also provides passive immunity to the baby in the form of maternal antibodies present in the milk.

Passage through the placenta of potentially harmful substances and of viruses.

Potentially harmful substances in the mother's blood can cross the placenta and have a number of adverse effects on the developing fetus. Such substances include nicotine, alcohol and heroin. Some viruses are also able to cross the placenta.

• Cigarette smoke contains numerous harmful substances including nicotine, tar and carbon monoxide. Maternal smoking adversely affects the fetus and decreases the chances of survival of the newborn infant, by decreasing the availability of oxygen to the fetus. It has been suggested that oxygen deprivation may be responsible for more than 30 per cent of the deaths of all stillborn infants and is a major cause of intrauterine growth retardation (IUGR).

• Alcohol is freely soluble and easily crosses the placenta. Consumption of alcohol during pregnancy can have tragic effects on the developing fetus. when alcohol enters the fetal blood, the result, called fetal alcohol syndrome (FAS) can cause congenital abnormalities such as microcephaly (abnormally small head), low birth weight, slow physical and mental development of the infant, or fetal death.

• Heroin. If the mother is addicted to heroin, then her baby probably will also be addicted. Such babies are very likely to be born underweight, or prematurely.

• Transmission of infection can also occur across the placenta, an example of vertical transmission. Microorganisms which can be transmitted in this way include the rubella virus, HIV, and the hepatitis B virus. The fetus is particularly susceptible to the rubella virus when maternal infection occurs during the first three months of pregnancy. The virus interferes with the development of the brain, heart, eyes and ears, resulting in a number of malformations, low birth weight, failure to thrive and increased infant mortality.

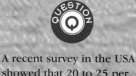

A recent survey in the USA showed that 20 to 25 per cent of women who smoked before pregnancy continued to do so. What are the public health issues associated with smoking (or drinking alcohol) during pregnancy? What factors might influence a woman's decision to continue to smoke during pregnancy?

Growth and physical development

The postnatal period begins at birth and lasts until death. Although it is often divided into four major periods, it is important to recognise that growth and development are continuous processes which occur throughout life. Gradual changes in the physical appearance of the body as a whole and in the relative proportions of the head, limbs and trunk are particularly noticeable between birth and adolescence. Figure 6.25 shows the changes in the relative proportions of the body parts of a boy from birth to 16 years.

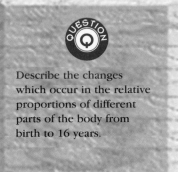

Describe the changes which occur in the relative proportions of different parts of the body from birth to 16 years.

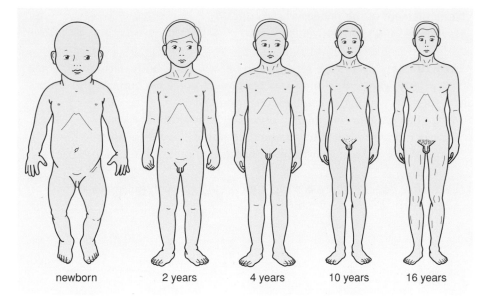

| newborn | 2 years | 4 years | 10 years | 16 years |

Figure 6.25 Changes in the proportions of body parts from birth to 16 years

Briefly, the postnatal periods are as follows:
1 Infancy, which begins at birth and lasts about 18 months.
2 Childhood, which extends from the end of infancy to sexual maturity, or puberty.
3 Adolescence and adulthood. The average age range of adolescence varies, but generally the teenage years (13 to 19) are used. This period is marked by rapid physical growth, resulting in sexual maturity.
4 Older adulthood, characterised by a gradual decline in every major organ system in the body.

Puberty is the age at which the reproductive organs reach maturity. In females, the ovaries are stimulated by the gonadotrophic hormones from the anterior pituitary, to secrete increasing amounts of oestrogen. Oestrogen, with progesterone, produces the changes of puberty. This occurs between the ages of about 10 and 14 years and the physical changes include:
• maturity of the uterus, oviducts and ovaries
• start of the menstrual cycle and ovulation
• development and enlargement of the breasts
• growth of pubic and axillary hair
• increase in the rate of growth in height
• widening of the pelvis
• increase in the amount of fat deposited in subcutaneous tissue.

Puberty in the male occurs between the ages of about 10 and 14 years. The gonadotrophic hormone ICSH (interstitial cell stimulating hormone) from the anterior pituitary stimulates production of testosterone in the testes. This hormone influences growth and development of the body to maturity. The physical changes which occur during puberty in the male include:
• growth of muscle and bone resulting in a marked increase in height
• the voice 'breaks', or deepens, due to growth of the larynx

- growth of pubic and axillary hair and of hair on the face, chest, abdomen
- enlargement of the penis and scrotum
- production of spermatozoa.

A **growth curve** shows the relationship between, say, body mass and the age of the person. Figure 6.26 shows such a growth curve for humans and, after birth, four distinct phases can be recognised:

1 A rapid increase during infancy, especially during the first year.
2 A slower, progressive increase from 3 to about 12 years of age.
3 A marked increase in growth from the time of puberty (the 'adolescent spurt').
4 Even after puberty, there is a slight increase in growth during early adulthood.

Figure 6.26 Growth curve for humans

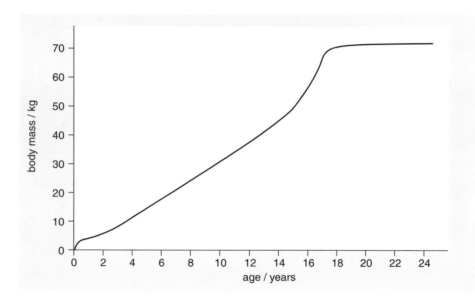

Control of fertility

At the end of the 20th century, world population has already exceeded five billion people. We have seen nearly a five-fold increase over the last 200 years, from an estimated one billion in 1830 and, at the current rate of increase, there will be a projected eight billion in the year 2030. Globally, this level of population growth exerts enormous pressure on the environment, in terms of our finite resources, on availability of food to feed the expanding population and on 'living space'. With continuing improvements in the standard of living throughout the globe, the pressures become greater. At a national level, there are political and economic reasons for limiting population growth. For individual people, there are personal reasons and social pressures for avoiding conception and limiting family size. (For fuller discussion of these topics, see *The Organism and the Environment, Second Edition.*)

Contraception

Control or limitation of family size is practised through deliberate measures taken before and after conception, including abstinence of intercourse, coitus interruptus, contraception and termination of pregnancy. Conception usually does not occur during lactation, since breast-feeding suppresses ovulation, making pregnancy less likely. The decision as to the method of contraception, and indeed whether or when to use it, rests with the individual – one or both of the partners engaging in sexual intercourse. The aim should be to ensure a high degree of safety (in terms of prevention of pregnancy), with minimum interference with the enjoyment of the sexual relationship and avoidance of side effects (either physical or physiological).

Barrier methods

A physical barrier can be used to prevent sperm meeting the ovum (oocyte). Usually this is either by means of a **condom** (latex sheath) placed over the man's erect penis or by insertion into the woman of a **diaphragm** or **cervical cap**, both of which cover the cervix and reduce the likelihood of sperm entering the uterus. Condoms for women, in the form of a sheath which lines the vagina, are also available though less widely used. The diaphragm should be the correct size for the woman and both the diaphragm and cervical cap must be left in place for some hours after use. When used in conjunction with a **spermicide** (chemical which kills sperms) these barrier methods offer a high degree of protection against conception. There are no side effects with respect to health of the individual, but care and a degree of responsibility must be taken in using them to ensure reliability. Condoms are widely (and sometimes freely) available, and their use is encouraged particularly with young people and those involved in casual sexual relationships, to avoid unwanted pregnancies. An important benefit in the use of condoms lies in the protection provided against transmission of sexually transmitted diseases, including AIDS.

Hormonal methods

Hormonal contraceptive methods aim to interfere with the natural hormone levels and particularly with gamete production. The main focus has been suppression of ovulation, though progress has been made with other forms of hormonal contraception. Development of oral contraception in the form of the 'pill' in the 1950s, represented a minor revolution for women. It enabled them to exercise far more control than ever before over the choice as to whether and when to have children, thus opening up greater opportunities to follow a career.

The contraceptive pill contains synthetic forms of **oestrogen** and **progesterone**, combined in different proportions. (Progesterone is one of a group of steroid hormones known as progestogens.) One version of the pill offers the same concentration of the two hormones for 21 days of a 28-day cycle, followed by 7 days with no hormone; a second version has a lower level of progestogen for the first 11 days and a third version has a three phase increase in progestogen together with slight increases in oestrogen for part of the cycle. These variations allow the hormones to mimic closely the effects of natural hormones involved in the menstrual cycle and keep the overall supplied dose at a low level. The raised level of these hormones act through negative feedback and the effect is, firstly, to suppress secretion of gonadotrophin releasing hormones (GnRH) from the hypothalamus. This in turn decreases the release of luteinising hormone (LH) and follicle stimulating

List reasons for changes in fertility and population increase during the 19th and 20th centuries. What are some of the pressures on the *environment* (at a local and at an international level) arising from population growth? Suggest reasons why *governments* may wish to minimise or to increase the nation's population growth. Think about why *individuals* may wish to limit or control their family size.

Refer to Figures 6.15, 6.20 and 6.22. For each method of contraception described in this section, locate precisely where it acts and how it interferes with the normal sequence of events.

hormone (FSH) from the anterior pituitary. It is the peaks of FSH and LH which trigger ovulation, so in the absence of this surge the ovarian follicles become less active and ovulation does not occur (see also figure 6.20).

In addition to suppressing ovulation, the hormones in the pill also influence changes in the histology of the endometrium (which normally occur during the menstrual cycle), making it unsuitable for implantation. A third effect, brought about by progestogen, is to increase the viscosity of the cervical mucus so that it becomes less receptive to sperms travelling to the uterus. This effect of progestogen in preventing implantation has led to the development of a pill containing progestogen only. Other longer term contraceptives are available to a limited extent, in forms which can be administered by injection, implanted say under the skin or impregnated into a ring placed in the vagina allowing slow release of the hormones. The "morning-after" pill (known as RU 486), if taken within three days of intercourse can prevent implantation. It acts as an antagonist to progesterone. Later in pregnancy, taking this pill results in abortion.

Women using the pill may experience side effects, some of which are beneficial while others increase the risk of certain conditions such as headaches, nausea and possible interference with the blood-clotting mechanisms. Compared with the early versions used in the 1950s, the modern low-dose forms of the pill have generally reduced the side effects. Appropriate advice should be obtained from a family planning clinic or doctor. When taken regularly as prescribed, the combined pill offers extremely reliable and safe contraception for women.

Interference with implantation

The use of hormones to reduce the likelihood of implantation are described in the section above (hormonal methods). The **intra-uterine device** (**IUD**) is a mechanical way of interfering with implantation of a fertilised ovum in the endometrium. The IUD consists of a plastic or metal coil or loop, placed in the uterus. It is inserted by a doctor through the cervix. It remains in place unless there is need for its removal. Some are coated with copper, which dissolves slowly and enhances the contraceptive action by inactivating sperm. Others may incorporate progestogen which is released gradually. There are risks of increased infections, heavier menstrual bleeding and occasional ectopic pregnancy (the fetus developing outside the normal position in the uterus), but for many women, the IUD offers reliable and trouble-free contraception.

Infertility and subfertility

A couple may be considered **infertile** if they have been unable to conceive after 12 months or more of unprotected sexual intercourse of average frequency. It is difficult to know the real extent of infertility, but it is estimated at around 15 per cent in couples in developed countries and perhaps double this proportion in developing countries. The prevalence in developing countries may be attributed to the high incidence of sexually transmitted diseases and poor hygiene at the time of earlier childbirth or abortion. Total infertility (or sterility) could be due to complete lack of either ova or sperm. For many couples, it is more helpful to consider the situation in terms of **subfertility**, or a lowering of fertility, in varying degrees.

Producing offspring is a natural part of biological behaviour and couples who are involuntarily childless often suffer overwhelming disappointment and distress. Since the 1970s, an increasing number of couples have sought treatment for infertility. This may represent a real increase in the number of infertile couples, but may also reflect a greater awareness of the development and potential of modern assisted reproductive technologies that could help a couple overcome their difficulties. Couples seeking advice must be prepared for a lengthy period of counselling and cannot be guaranteed a positive outcome. However, with continuing research and greater understanding of reproductive biology, there is increasing hope of success.

Infertility can be linked to any of the events which would normally result in successful conception – from production of ovum and sperm, to their meeting in the oviduct after sexual intercourse, allowing fertilisation followed by implantation in the endometrium of the uterus. The causes of infertility most commonly encountered are:

- in the woman – failure to ovulate; obstruction of the oviduct(s) (Fallopian tubes); disease of the endometrium; hostile cervical mucus; infections
- in the man – absence of sperm; decrease in numbers of sperm (which may include a higher proportion of abnormal sperm); decreased motility of sperm; blockage in any part of the male reproductive tract.

In the woman, failure to ovulate is usually a result of hormone imbalance. Treatment with certain drugs, which mimic the action of natural hormones, can help restore the stimulus to the pituitary to enable it to secrete sufficient FSH and LH to trigger events in the ovary which lead to ovulation. Obstruction of the oviduct(s) can often be corrected by surgery.

In the man, blockage of the epididymis or ductus deferens (sperm ducts) prevents the maturation or passage of sperm and so reduces fertility. The tubes are extremely narrow but microsurgery can sometimes successfully overcome this. A far more common reason for infertility in the man is a reduction in numbers of 'normal' sperm in the semen of his ejaculate. Even at normal fertility levels, there is a high proportion of abnormal or distorted sperm cells. An average ejaculate of 2.5 to 3.5 cm^3 contains between 60 and 150 million active sperm per cm^3 of semen. Numbers of active sperm below about 30 million per cm^3 are an indication of infertility.

Various environmental factors appear to contribute to a reduction in numbers of viable sperm. These include over-heating of the testes (hot baths or tight clothing), as well as tiredness, stress, smoking, caffeine and alcohol. Pesticides and other chemicals used in the environment have been linked with reduced fertility in both men and women. Strenuous physical exercise, as carried out by athletes or ballet dancers, is often associated with menstrual irregularity or absence. Fertility declines with age: women show their peak during their early 20s, and this declines during their 30s. Ovulation ceases after menopause, usually in their early 50s. Reduced fertility in a population as a whole may be a reflection of the trend to delay starting a family, for example until the woman has had an opportunity to develop a career or for economic reasons.

Assisted reproduction – artificial insemination and in vitro fertilisation

Louise Brown, born in 1978, was the first 'test tube' baby. Conception was assisted by **in vitro fertilisation** (**IVF**) and her birth represented a landmark in the development of techniques which can help infertile couples.

Artificial insemination (**AI**) is used routinely in animal husbandry, particularly in cattle breeding programmes: its application to humans has made important contributions to successful conception in otherwise infertile couples. The steps in the procedure for IVF are summarised in Figure 6.27.

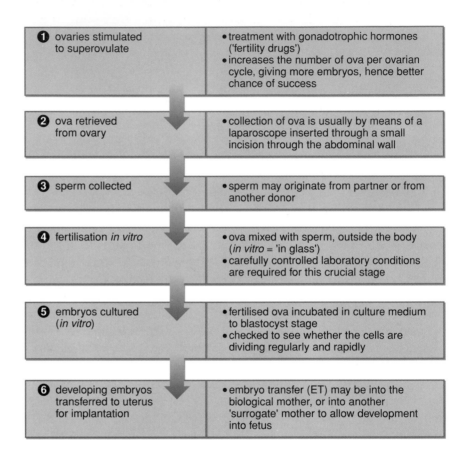

❶ ovaries stimulated to superovulate	• treatment with gonadotrophic hormones ('fertility drugs') • increases the number of ova per ovarian cycle, giving more embryos, hence better chance of success
❷ ova retrieved from ovary	• collection of ova is usually by means of a laparoscope inserted through a small incision through the abdominal wall
❸ sperm collected	• sperm may originate from partner or from another donor
❹ fertilisation *in vitro*	• ova mixed with sperm, outside the body (*in vitro* = 'in glass') • carefully controlled laboratory conditions are required for this crucial stage
❺ embryos cultured (*in vitro*)	• fertilised ova incubated in culture medium to blastocyst stage • checked to see whether the cells are dividing regularly and rapidly
❻ developing embryos transferred to uterus for implantation	• embryo transfer (ET) may be into the biological mother, or into another 'surrogate' mother to allow development into fetus

Figure 6.27 Outline of steps in procedure for in vitro *fertilisation (IVF)*

Within the framework of IVF, there are variations in how and when assistance is given, depending on the cause of infertility. Some of these are outlined below.

- **gamete intrafallopian transfer** (**GIFT**) – the ova and sperm are both collected and then placed together in the oviduct (Fallopian tube), where fertilisation may take place, followed by implantation in the endometrium
- **zygote intrafallopian transfer** (**ZIFT**) – fertilisation occurs externally, but the zygote is then immediately placed in the oviduct where cell division starts, followed by movement to the uterus for implantation
- **oocyte donation** - when an 'infertile' woman cannot produce ova (oocytes), donated ova from another woman may be fertilised by the partner's sperm. The embryo can then be placed into the uterus of the

infertile woman, where development and pregnancy may continue normally. The child would be biologically related to one of the parents.

Artificial insemination may be carried out with the partner's (husband's) sperm (**HI**) or with sperm derived from a donor (**DI**). In the latter case, the child would be biologically related to one of the parents, and this may be an acceptable course of action where the man has a very low sperm count. When collecting semen from a man for artificial insemination, the semen is generally centrifuged and treated so that the concentration of sperm is increased and the sample checked to ensure it contains adequate numbers of high quality sperm with suitable motility. It is introduced by a small syringe, either into the woman's vagina or higher through the cervix into the uterus. AI may be successful when the woman's cervix has a hostile reaction to sperm, if the man has a low sperm count or when he is unable to have normal intercourse, for example because of spinal injury.

Success rates in assisted reproduction are still relatively low: GIFT ~18-26 per cent, ZIFT ~17 per cent and IVF ~13 per cent per cycle (some clinics claim up to 30 per cent, but this may be linked to careful selection of potential parents). While successful conception may bring happiness to otherwise infertile couples, the practices of assisted reproduction and research with human embryos represent an area of extreme sensitivity which is ethically controversial. Some people, for religious or personal reasons, disagree with any form of contraception, abortion or interference with the so-called natural processes of reproduction. There is the danger that, if used irresponsibly, there could be selection of sexes which would upset the balance within a population, or indiscriminate use of donor gametes could accidentally result in biologically close relatives producing children. Traditional taboos against incest or marriage between close relatives are an ancient way of minimising the chance of genetic defects appearing within a family. In the UK, the Human Fertilisation and Embryology Act in 1990 laid down guidelines for legal aspects of children produced by artificial insemination and IVF and also established the Human Fertilisation Embryology Authority (HFEA). The legal parents of children produced by assisted conception are not necessarily the biological parents and at some stage, the children may wish to know their true biological parents. The HFEA requires registration of all people whose gametes are used for assisted reproduction and all children produced by assisted reproduction and also controls and reviews research with human embryos.

Genetic counselling

Developments in molecular biology and medical research are giving us a greater understanding of a range of disorders or diseases which have a genetic cause and can therefore be inherited. **Genetic counsellors** try to help individuals to find out about the risk to themselves or to their children of suffering from a genetic disorder. When the possible risk has been established, or a genetic condition confirmed, the counselling process will try to help the person or family decide what action to take, to learn what treatment may be available or sometimes just to come to terms with a difficult and distressing situation. The investigation and counselling process is likely to involve doctors, geneticists, biochemists and other analysts as well as social workers.

In China there is the 'one-child' policy and there is global pressure for control of population growth, yet successes in IVF (in vitro fertilisation) are heralded as front page news. Outline the options available through IVF for couples with low fertility. How far do you feel that research into reproductive technology is justified? Indicate some of the ethical and moral issues involved in its use in society.

Figure 6.28 A laparoscope is an illuminated tube which is passed through a small incision in the body wall and can allow examination of structures inside the abdomen. This instrument can be used to collect ova from the ovary for in vitro fertilisation

Causes of genetic disorders

Genetic disorders may result from defects or abnormalities at the level of the **chromosomes** or within the individual **genes**. The estimated prevalence of disorders caused directly by these genetic abnormalities is in the region of 20 per 1000 population, though other conditions such as coronary heart disease, diabetes and cancer have strong genetic links. Chromosome abnormalities may be due to changes in chromosome number or to structural defects, such as deletion or translocation. Abnormalities may be recognised from the **karyotype** of an affected individual. Many gross defects probably do not survive and may be a cause of early spontaneous abortion of a fetus. Defects at the single gene level follow a Mendelian pattern of inheritance, expressed either in the **autosomes** or in the **sex (X or Y) chromosomes**, and may affect the dominant or the recessive allele. As a result of the Human Genome Project (a huge international research programme in which all the human genes are being mapped), the position of many of the genes has now been located on a particular chromosome and detailed DNA analysis has allowed yet more precise mapping of the genes on the chromosome. Some examples of genetic disorders, their causes and descriptions of how they may affect people are given in Table 6.5.

Family history and risk of inheriting genetic disorders

A couple who know of an inherited disease in a near relative may seek advice through genetic counselling before deciding to start a family. With an understanding of Mendelian inheritance it may be possible to trace the family history through pedigree analysis and work out the risk of an inherited disorder passing to their children (see Figure 6.29). Estimation of risk may alter depending on the age at which the onset of the disorder usually occurs. It may also be important to identify **carriers** – such people carry the affected allele but show no symptoms of the disorder. The risk of chromosome abnormalities increases with age of the mother, so, for example, the risk of Down's syndrome in babies born to mothers over the age of 35 years is considerably higher than that for younger women.

Detection of fetal abnormalities

Prenatal tests may be undertaken to allow detection of abnormalities in the fetus. Procedures commonly used include **ultrasound scanning**, **amniocentesis** and **chorionic villus sampling** (Figure 6.30). When some fetal material has been obtained, tests can be carried out to determine whether or not there are chromosomal or genetic defects and to identify them as far as possible. A **karyotype** is obtained by treating extracted cells so that the chromosomes become visible and they are then photographed. The chromosomes are cut out then arranged and numbered (from 1 to 22) in order of size, starting with the largest, and followed by the sex chromosomes (X and Y).

DNA analysis is now becoming a standard procedure for locating particular gene defects and for identifying carriers. The pattern of bases in a DNA molecule can be achieved using the technique known as **DNA profiling**. The DNA is extracted from the fetal material, then cut into lengths using enzymes. The enzymes which cut DNA are known as **restriction enzymes**, and these enzymes recognise particular sequences so can be chosen to cut the DNA

Table 6.5 *Genetic disorders – causes and descriptions in affected person*

Example	Cause and description of affected person
Chromosome abnormalities	
numerical defects	
Down's syndrome	• trisomy (2n + 1) of chromosome 21. Characteristic flat face with slanting eyes, broad hands, short in height, varying degrees of mental retardation, likelihood of other conditions such as heart defects and deafness
Turner's syndrome	• monosomy (2n – 1) of X chromosome (XO). Females, but infertile as no ovaries, short in height and may have webbed appearance of the neck
Klinefelter's syndrome	• 47 chromosomes (XXY). Males, but small testes and usually infertile (no sperm production). tall and thin, possibly some development of breasts, sometimes mild mental retardation
structural defects	
'cri du chat' syndrome	• deletion of short arm of chromosome 5. Mental retardation, multiple physical abnormalities, characteristic cry (like a cat)
fragile X syndrome	• fragile site on chromosome X. Mental retardation, abnormal head and face including high forehead
Gene abnormalities	
autosomal dominant disorders	
achondroplasia	• dwarfism due to a defect in cartilage and bones so they fail to grow to the correct size. Intelligence, head and body size are all normal
Huntington's disease (chromosome 4)	• involuntary jerky movements of the head, progressing into dementia. Starts to appear in early middle age
adult polycystic kidney disease (chromosome 16)	• cysts in the kidney, may lead to kidney failure
autosomal recessive disorders	
cystic fibrosis (chromosome 7)	• lacks the protein which allows transport of chloride ions across cell membranes. Production of thick mucus likely to affect pancreas, bronchi, sweat glands, etc. Frequent respiratory infections
galactosaemia (chromosome 9)	• unable to utilise galactose (derived from lactose, but normally converted to glucose in liver). If untreated, babies become mentally retarded, but develop normally if fed on a galactose-free diet
phenylketonuria (chromosome 12)	• has excess of the amino acid phenylalanine which damages the nervous system leading to mental retardation. If detected early, babies are fed on a diet free of protein containing phenylalanine
sickle cell disease (chromosome 11)	• produces abnormal sickle-cell haemoglobin (HbS), leading to distortion of the red blood cells and may result in anaemia. The defect is due to substitution of valine for glutamic acid in one chain in the haemoglobin molecule
X linked recessive disorders	
colour blindness	• most commonly as a failure to distinguish between reds and greens
Duchenne muscular dystrophy	• weakness and wasting of muscles, especially of the back and pelvic girdle. Starts before the age of four. Can be relieved but not cured by physiotherapy and orthopaedic treatment
haemophilia	• blood clots very slowly because of lack of coagulating factors, known as Factor VIII and Factor IX. Person may suffer prolonged bleeding after wounding or spontaneous internal bleeding. Treatment by blood transfusion or supplying missing factor(s)

molecule in a specific place. The fragments of DNA are loaded onto an agarose gel, then separated by electrophoresis. The resulting patterns of banding of the DNA fragments can be revealed by treatment with radioactive labels or dyes. Techniques are also available to work out the actual sequence of bases along a length of DNA. (For further details see *The Organism and the Environment, Second Edition*.)

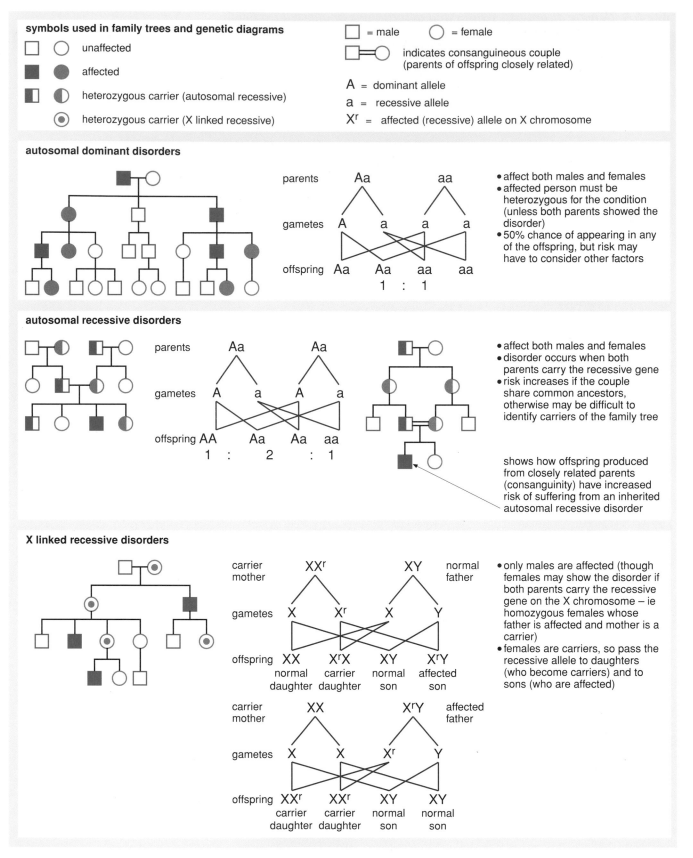

Figure 6.29 Family pedigrees - showing inheritance of autosomal dominant disorders, autosomal recessive, X linked recessive dominant disorders, X linked dominant and Y linked dominant disorders

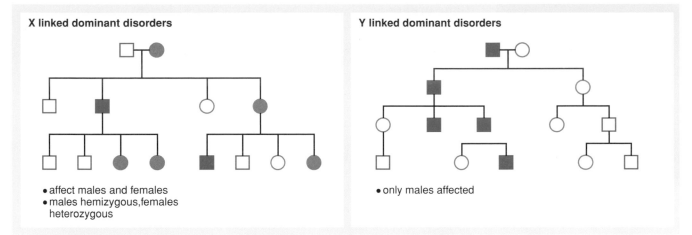

X linked dominant disorders

- affect males and females
- males hemizygous, females heterozygous

Y linked dominant disorders

- only males affected

Figure 6.29 Family pedigrees - showing inheritance of autosomal dominant, autosomal recessive, X linked recessive dominant disorders, X linked dominant and Y linked

ultra sound scanning
- uses high frequency sound waves to build up picture on TV screen of features within the body
- confirms viable pregnancy
- locates placenta
- monitors fetal growth
- detects major deformities

amniocentesis
- sample of amniotic fluid containing fetal cells withdrawn through the abdominal wall
- amniotic cells can be cultured for further tests
- biochemical analysis on fluid or cultured cells for diagnosis of errors of metabolism
- cells can yield karyotype to see chromosome pattern
- analysis of DNA to locate specific gene defects
- results from fluid in about one week, from cultured cells in about 3 to 4 weeks
- performed at about 15 to 16 weeks' gestation
- reliable and safe with low risk of increasing miscarriage

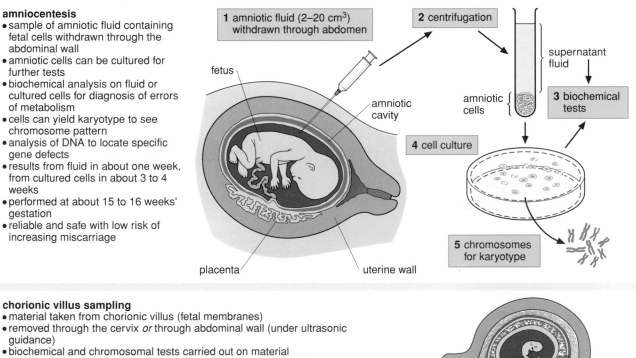

1 amniotic fluid (2–20 cm^3) withdrawn through abdomen

2 centrifugation

supernatant fluid

fetus

amniotic cavity

amniotic cells

3 biochemical tests

4 cell culture

5 chromosomes for karyotype

placenta

uterine wall

chorionic villus sampling
- material taken from chorionic villus (fetal membranes)
- removed through the cervix *or* through abdominal wall (under ultrasonic guidance)
- biochemical and chromosomal tests carried out on material
- culturing of cells not needed (so results obtained more quickly than amniocentesis)
- performed at between 9 and 12 weeks' gestation
- risk of miscarriage slightly higher than normal at this time

Figure 6.30 Prenatal testing of fetus – outline of ultrasound scanning, amniocentesis and chorionic villus sampling

Figure 6.31 With advances in DNA technology, many genes on the human chromosomes have now been mapped, including the location of certain genetic disorders. Analysis of selected portions of DNA can lead to detection of mutant alleles, indicating specific genetic disorders. The photo shows autoradiagrams of DNA fragments, separated by electrophoresis, being inspected on a lightbox

Find out about DNA technology ... and how it helps detect genetic defects.

• Why is the polymerase chain reaction (PCR) important in DNA analysis?

• How is the DNA sample broken into fragments?

• What technique is used to separate the DNA fragments?

• How is the gene defect identified?

(as a hint, look at accounts of DNA fingerprinting, or refer to *The Organism and the Environment, Second Edition*, Chapter 9)

Gene probes can be used to identify particular sequences in the DNA molecule. A probe is a short length of nucleotides with unique base sequences which binds to and hybridises with particular portions of a complementary molecule of DNA. In detection of genetic defects, the probe is chosen to correspond to and recognise regions where the faulty base sequence is suspected. Probes are now used successfully to detect conditions such as Huntington's disease, cystic fibrosis, Duchenne muscular dystrophy and phenylketonuria.

Social, ethical and legal considerations

As research developments in reproductive biology continue, individuals and couples have more and more control over their own reproduction: if and when to have children, means of overcoming infertility, understanding of the risk of producing children with genetic disorders, knowledge of whether a fetus has certain genetic abnormalities. With the information available, individuals need to make decisions, as to whether to start a family or to have further children, whether to terminate a pregnancy in which genetic defects have been confirmed or take advantage of the treatment available to help the affected new born baby live and grow through to adulthood. The decisions often need to be made within a framework of informed advice, with guidance from medical experts and consideration of the legal requirements as well as personal and often religious beliefs. For the people involved in a reproductive dilemma, to come to a decision may be emotional and stressful and it may take time and sympathetic understanding to come to terms with the situation.

For those faced with risk or reality of genetic defects in their children, genetic counselling aims to help individuals go through all aspects of the situation. Studies of family history allow an assessment of risk and may suggest priority is given to prenatal testing. Genetic screening before pregnancy can detect carriers in unaffected people and be offered to the individuals concerned as well as to close relatives. Genetic screening by tests during pregnancy may be offered to those most at risk and as more tests become available through DNA analysis, it is likely that prenatal screening will be used to diagnose a wide range of possible defects. It is essential that the tests are reliable and that the results are accurate: to obtain either false negative or false positive information would be extremely distressing. It is important for the tests to be carried out early in pregnancy, partly to relieve anxiety for the pregnant mother and her partner but also so that there is opportunity for termination of pregnancy before the 13th week, if possible, if it is decided to take this course of action. In this respect, chorionic villus sampling is an improvement over amniocentesis though it carries an increased risk of spontaneous abortion.

Termination of pregnancy by abortion may be **spontaneous** (also known as miscarriage) or **induced** artifically. It is estimated that about 15 to 20 per cent of conceptions end in spontaneous abortion, often within the first three months of pregnancy, and probably half of these carry chromosomal abnormalities. Induced abortion may be carried out surgically or by administering drugs such as prostaglandins which cause uterine contractions so that the immature fetus is expelled. When undertaken with good medical care, induced abortions are generally safe. However, many illegal abortions, particularly those used as a form of contraception for unwanted pregnancies, are performed in unhygienic conditions which can be dangerous for the mother.

In the UK, induced abortion can only be performed within the terms of the Abortion Act (1967) and later legal Abortion Regulations. The requirements are for two doctors to agree to termination of the pregnancy, for reasons stated in the Act, and for it to be carried out in an approved hospital or clinic. Even so, some people, for personal or religious reasons will not agree to have an abortion and there is continuing active debate as to the stage at which the fetus has the 'rights' of a person. Some believe it is at the moment of fertilisation, other people accept abortion right up to the moment of delivery of the fetus if it is in the interest of the physical or mental health of the mother, or if there is a significant risk that if the fetus is born it will suffer from a serious physical or mental handicap. In some countries (for example, the Republic of Ireland and Portugal), therapeutic abortion is illegal at all stages whereas other countries have more liberal pro-abortion policies. In the UK, the 1967 Abortion Act allowed abortion (for specified reasons) up to 28 weeks of gestation, though more recently this limit has been relaxed in certain cases. Inevitably the debate will continue and one factor to be considered is that babies born as early as 23 weeks can now survive. This emphasises the need for accurate diagnosis of potential defects to be made early in pregnancy and for informed counselling to help the couple come to a decision which is consistent with their personal beliefs and the legal constraints.

While medical technology allows manipulation of reproduction and inevitably raises ethical dilemmas, it also offers treatment or cures for some of the genetic disorders which can be detected by prenatal screening. Galactosaemia and phenylketonuria (PKU) are conditions that can both be controlled by careful selection of diet. For sufferers from galactosaemia, it is essential for the baby to receive a galactose-free or lactose-free diet soon after birth, and probably for life, so avoiding development of permanent mental retardation and other symptoms. Similarly, those affected by PKU can be treated by limiting the intake in the diet of the amino acid phenylalanine. For some conditions, it may be possible to supply the missing gene product and examples here include treatment for haemophilia, growth hormone deficiency and insulin deficiency.

For many genetic disorders for which there is no permanent cure or relief, there is a network of support groups for families and such groups often offer advice or information which may help the family come to terms with the condition and allow the best quality of life available for the affected person. Details of the support network may be obtained through: *Contact a family, 16 Strutton Ground, London SW1P 2HP.*

A further prospect for cure for people with genetic defects, and one which is undergoing active (and controversial) research, is the use of **gene therapy**. This utilises gene technology to incorporate a portion of DNA carrying the required correct base sequence into the genome of the affected person so that the genetic defect is effectively repaired. At the time of writing (1997) clinical trials are in progress for gene therapy for cystic fibrosis patients. While this approach has considerable potential for offering hope to sufferers, at the same time it raises ethical concerns over manipulation of the human genome and how far medical research can go. As with research on human embryos and the possibilities in the future for cloning of human beings, we need to give very careful thought concerning the controls to be set up to ensure the techniques are used in a responsible manner. There is no doubt that the technology is there, or will be in the forseeable future, but how it is used remains a personal as well as a legal decision, and one that needs debate on an international scale to provide appropriate safeguards for our future societies.

We need to keep in perspective the research advances and future potential of reproductive and DNA technologies. At one time, Edward Jenner was a brave man to experiment with the use of cowpox vaccine to provide immunity against the infectious disease of smallpox. Despite initial and continuing controversy, Jenner's trials resulted in development of vaccines which have led to worldwide eradication of smallpox. We now accept heart bypass operations and organ transplant surgery as realistic ways of prolonging and improving the quality of life for sufferers of certain medical conditions. Yet at the time of the first attempts, the pioneers required considerable faith in their research developments and had to withstand controversial debate before they achieved a degree of success. However, there will always be some people who cannot accept interference with natural events in the human body and disagree with any form of artificial contraception, termination of pregnancy or even diagnosis of genetic defects. Their views must be respected. Others are prepared to move forward with the frontiers of scientific knowledge, but application of biological technology must be in the context of informed debate and responsible decision making.

The sequence of events in mammalian reproduction is largely regulated by hormones.

- List the main hormones which influence reproduction in humans
- Which of these show activity in males and which in females? Do any of them have influence in both?
- Where is each hormone produced? What triggers its production?
- For each hormone, list the target(s) it acts upon and then give its effect(s). Which stimulate the production of other hormones and which act directly on an organ?
- How far can the control of reproduction by hormones be used as an example of negative feedback? (Look back at the chart in chapter 3, page 69).
- In what ways are hormones used artificially to control reproductive events? Think about prevention of conception as well as overcoming low fertility.

Examination questions

Chapter 1

1   Describe the following processes which occur during urine formation in
    mammals.
    (a) Ultrafiltration   (2 marks)
    (b) Selective reabsorption of glucose   (2 marks)

                                                          (Total 4 marks)

2   Compare the mechanisms for gas exchange in flowering plants and animals.

                                                          (Total 10 marks)

Chapter 2

1   The table below refers to three different plant cells found in stems.
    Complete the table by writing the appropriate word or words in the empty
    boxes.

Cell type	*One* characteristic structural feature	*One* function
Sieve tube element		
		Transport of water and mineral ions
	Walls thickened in the corners	Support

                                                          (Total 5 marks)

2   An investigation was carried out into the absorption of mineral ions by
    beech tree seedlings. The absorption of phosphate ions by beech roots was
    measured in moist air, and in an atmosphere of moist nitrogen.

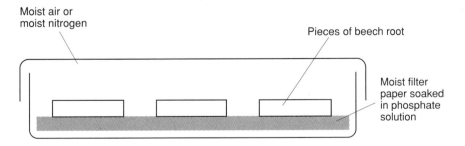

The results are shown in the graph on page 154.

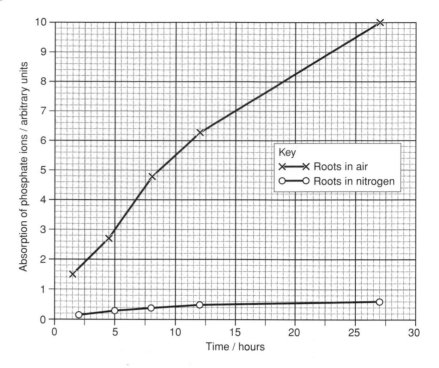

(a) Calculate the rate of absorption of phosphate ions by beech roots in air between 10 hours and 20 hours. Show your working. (3 marks)

(b) (i) Compare the rates of absorption of phosphate ions by roots in air and roots in nitrogen. (2 marks)

(ii) Suggest an explanation for the difference in rates of absorption. (2 marks)

(c) (i) Suggest *two* reasons why the atmosphere in which the roots are kept has to be moist. (2 marks)

(ii) Suggest *two* factors that should be kept constant in this experiment (2 marks)

(Total 11 marks)

3 The diagram below shows a section of human heart at a specific stage in the cardiac cycle.

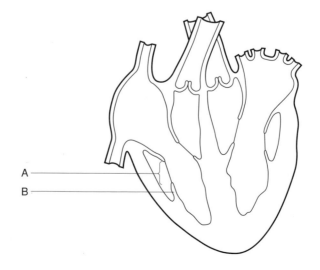

(a) Name the stage of the cardiac cycle shown in the diagram and give
     two reasons for your choice.   (3 marks)
(b) Give *one* function of each of the parts A and B.

Part	Function
A	
B	

(2 marks)

(Total 5 marks)

4 All the cells in the blood come from just one type of cell, the *multipotential
   stem cell*. When the stem cell divides one of the two daughter cells may go
   on to give rise to other types of cell, whereas the other daughter cell
   remains a stem cell.

Adapted from The triumph of the embryo, *Wolpert 1991*

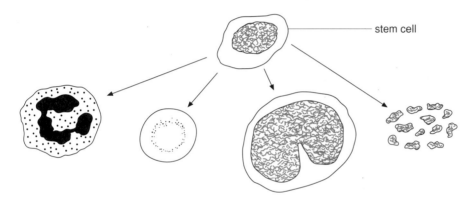

(a) Suggest *one* region of the body where the stem cells referred to in
     the above extract are formed.   (1 mark)
(b) Name *two* types of blood cells that are phagocytic.   (2 marks)
(c) Which cellular component of blood begins the process of blood
     clotting?   (1 mark)
(d) Suggest why, when a stem cell divides, it is important that one
     daughter cell remains a stem cell.   (1 mark)

(Total 5 marks)

Chapter 3

1 The statements on page 156 refer to some effects of two groups of plant
   growth substances, auxins and gibberellins. If the statement is correct place
   a tick (✓) in the appropriate box and if the statement is incorrect place a
   cross (✗) in the appropriate box.

Effect	Auxins	Gibberellins
Promote cell elongation		
Promote root formation in cuttings and calluses		
Promote fruit ripening		
Inhibit lateral bud development		
Promote the breaking of dormancy in seeds		

(Total 5 marks)

2 An investigation was carried out into the effect of cytokinin on cell division in cultures of soya bean tissue. Uniform pieces of soya bean tissue were added to artificial media either with or without cytokinin, and the number of cells in each culture was estimated each day for six days. The results are shown in the graph below. Each figure is the mean of eight measurements.

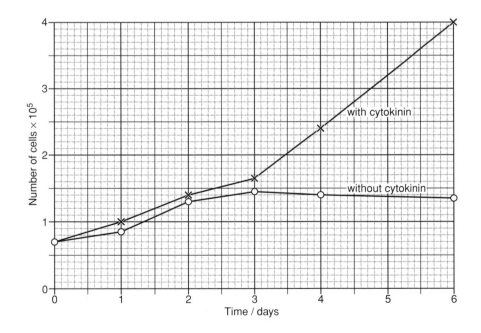

Adapted from Fosket and Short, Physiol. plant. 28: 14–23, 1973

(a) (i) From the graph determine the difference in numbers of cells in the cultures with and without cytokinin on day 5. Show your working. (2 marks)

(ii) Comment on the results as shown in the graph, including any conclusions that may be drawn concerning the effect of cytokinin on cell division. (3 marks)

(b) It was suggested that cytokinin might exert its full effect on cell division by stimulating the replication of DNA.

To investigate this suggestion, soya bean tissue cultures were grown on media containing different concentrations of cytokinin. The DNA content of each culture was measured after six days

Cytokinin in medium / mol dm^{-3}	DNA content of tissue culture / mg per million cells
0	3.90
10^{-7}	2.15
10^{-5}	1.90

    (i) Do the data in the table support the suggestion that cytokinin exerts its effect on cell division by stimulating DNA replication? Explain your answer. (2 marks)

    (ii) Suggest an explanation for the effect of cytokinin concentration on the DNA content of the dividing cells in these tissue cultures. (2 marks)

(c) Plant tissue culture media contain auxins in addition to cytokinins. Explain why the combination of the two plant growth substances is used. (2 marks)

(Total 11 marks)

Chapter 4

1 Read through the following passage about the mammalian nervous system, then write on the dotted lines the most appropriate word or words to complete the account.

The nervous system contains several types of neurones. Of these .... neurones carry impulses to muscles and glands while .... neurones carry impulses from receptor cells to the central nervous system. The interior of a nerve fibre has a lower concentration of .... ions than its surroundings, as a result of the action of a .... in its membrane. This imbalance of ions creates a .... potential in the fibre, which is reversed during the passage of an impulse. When this happens, ... ions flood into the fibre, after which there is a compensating outward movement of.......... ions. (Total 7 marks)

2 (a) Describe the sequence of events that takes place when a nerve impulse arrives at a synapse. (4 marks)

    (b) The diagram on page 158 shows the changes in membrane potential in a presynaptic neurone and postsynaptic neurone when an impulse passes across a synapse.

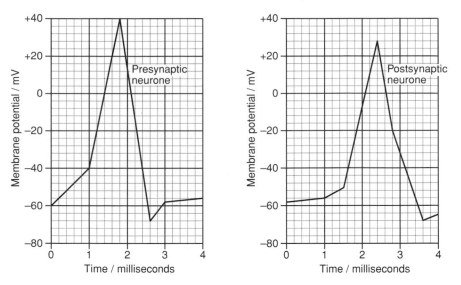

(i) Explain how depolarisation ocurs in the presynaptic neurone.

(3 marks)

(ii) The maximum depolarisation in the presynaptic neurone is +40 mV. What is the maximum depolarisation in the postsynaptic neurone? (1 mark)

(iii) How long is the delay between the maximum depolarisation in the presynaptic and postsynaptic neurones? (1 mark)

(iv) What is the cause of this delay? (1 mark)

(c) Describe how nicotine affects synaptic transmission. (2 marks)

(Total 12 marks)

Chapter 5

1 The table below refers to the structure and functions of xylem vessels and phloem sieve tubes in plants.

If the statement is correct, place a tick (✓) in the appropriate box and if the statement is incorrect, place a cross (✗) in the appropriate box.

Statement	Xylem vessels	Phloem sieve tubes
Possess living contents		
Provide support		
Composed of cells fused together end to end		
Walls contain lignin		

(Total 4 marks)

2 The diagram below shows a sarcomere from a myofibril of a striated muscle fibre.

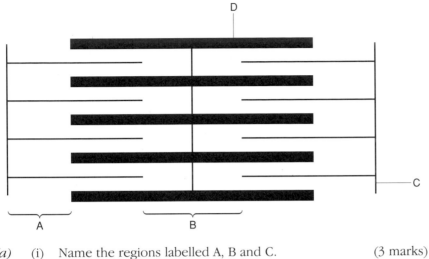

(a) (i) Name the regions labelled A, B and C. (3 marks)
 (ii) Name the material which makes up part D. (1 mark)
(b) State the change in appearance of B when the muscle fibre contracts
 (1 mark)

(Total 5 marks)

3 Read through the following passage, which refers to different types of skeleton in various animal groups, then write on the dotted lines the most appropriate word or words to complete the account.

A .... skeleton is typical of earthworms. Insects have an .... skeleton, which contains a material called .... The skeletons of mammals, however, are found .... their bodies, and are made of bone, which is strengthened with mineral ions such as .... and ....

(Total 6 marks)

Chapter 6

1 Read through the following account of the hormonal control of the human menstrual cycle and then write on the dotted lines the most appropriate word or words to complete the account.

The release of .... from the anterior pituitary gland induces the development of primary follicles. Another hormone from the anterior pituitary gland stimulates the thecal cells to produce ...., which controls the repair of the .... after menstruation. At ovulation, a .... is released from the mature follicle. The remaining follicular cells form the .... which begins to secrete ...., inhibiting the release of the hormones from the anterior pituitary gland.

(Total 6 marks)

2 The diagram below shows the structure of part of a mammalian placenta and the umbilical cord, which is attached to a developing fetus.

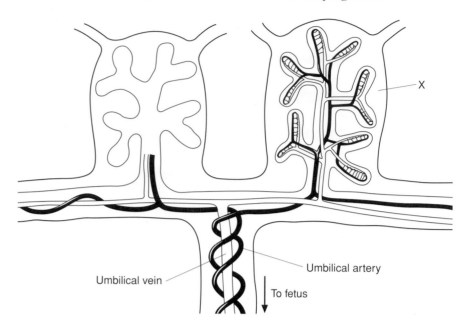

(a) State *two* substances which would be present in a higher concentration in the umbilical vein than in the umbilical artery.

(2 marks)

(b) The cavity labelled X contains maternal blood. Suggest why it is an advantage for this blood to be in a cavity rather than in a vessel.

(2 marks)

(Total 4 marks)

3 Records of human fertility for the period 1930 to 1990 have shown changes in the sperm counts of normal men.

The table below summarises the changing percentages of men with high or low sperm counts over the period of sixty years.

High sperm count $> 100 \times 10^6$ sperm cm^{-3}

Low sperm count $< 20 \times 10^6$ sperm cm^{-3}

Time period	Men with high sperm counts / %	Men with low sperm counts / %
1930–1950	50	5
1951–1960	45	4
1961–1970	28	14
1971–1980	21	11
1981–1990	15	18

(a) (i) Comment on the changes in the percentage of men with high sperm counts during the period 1930 to 1990. (2 marks)

(ii) Compare the figures for men with low sperm counts with those for high sperm counts over the same period. (3 marks)

(b) Explain why it is necessary for large numbers of sperms to be produced when only one sperm is required to bring about fertilisation. (2 marks)

(c) Exposure of pregnant women to high levels of certain oestrogens during early pregnancy can result in reproductive disorders in their male offspring.

It appears that a number of compounds in the environment can mimic the action of oestrogens when ingested. Such compounds, termed oestrogenic chemicals, are found in pesticides such as DDT and PCBs, and also in the breakdown products of certain detergents. They accumulate in the fatty tissue and have the same effect as oestrogens, which play a major role in the menstrual cycle.

(i) Describe the normal role of oestrogens in the menstrual cycle. (3 marks)

(ii) Suggest how the oestrogenic chemicals pass from the mother to the developing fetus. (3 marks)

(Total 13 marks)

4 Give an account of the adaptations of flowers to insect and wind pollination as illustrated by the flowers of the Papilionaceae and a grass.

(Total 10 marks)

Mark schemes

Edexcel Foundation, London Examinations accepts no responsibility whatsoever for the accuracy or method of working in the answers given. In the mark schemes, the following symbols are used :
; indicates separate marking points
/ indicates alternative marking points
eq means correct equivalent points are accepted

Chapter 1

1 (a) blood under high pressure in glomerulus / eq ; molecules of low molecular weight / small molecules ; pass through basement membrane / and / or / capillary wall ; into Bowman's capsule ; (2 marks)

   (b) in proximal / primary convoluted tubule ; carriers / pumps (in membrane) ; active transport / needs energy / ATP / reference to mitochondria / brush border qualified / microvilli qualified ; into capillaries / blood ;   (2 marks)
                                                                                          (Total 4 marks)

2 gas exchange in both takes place over respiratory surface ; reference to lungs in mammals ; reference to (spongy) mesophyll of leaves in plants ; access to respiratory surface via trachea / bronchi / eq in mammals ; aclenticels / corky tissue in woody stems ; active drawing in of air / ventilation mechanism in mammals ; credit for details of ventilation mechanism ; passive movement / diffusion of gases in plants ; respiratory surface / gas exchange surface must be large ; reference to alveoli in mammals (as large surface) ; reference to spongy mesophyll in flowering plants (as large surface) ; thin surfaces aid rapid diffusion / short diffusion paths ; alveoli one cell thick in mammals ; thin cell walls in mesophyll of plants ; moist surfaces aid diffusion of gases / eq ; film of moisture lines alveolar surface ; plant cell walls moist ; respiratory surfaces must be permeable to gases ; capillary network around alveoli /eq in mammals ; maintains high concentration gradient / eq; enables more rapid / higher diffusion rate ;

                                                                                          (Total 10 marks)

Chapter 2

1

Cell type	*One* characteristic structural feature	*One* function
Sieve tube element	sieve plate / no nucleus / few organelles ;	translocation / transport of sucrose / amino acids ;
vessel / tracheid ;	lignified / no cell contents / no end walls (if vessel) ;	Transport of water and mineral ions
collenchyma cell ;	Walls thickened in the corners	Support

                                                                                          (Total 5 marks)

2 (*a*) 8.3 or 8.2 – 5.5 or 5.6 ; 2.6 to 2.8/10/ ; / = 0.26 to 0.28 arbitrary units hr^{-1} ;

    (*b*) (i)   higher / eq in air / lower in nitrogen; correct reference to figures / highest level of absorption in nitrogen lower than lowest level in air ; both rates approximately constant / linear / rise steadily ;

                                     (2 marks)

          (ii) oxygen (from air) available for respiration ; provides energy ; for active uptake of phosphate ions ;   (2 marks)

    (*c*) (i)   uptake of oxygen / gas exchange / diffusion easier if moist ; water needed for absorption of ions / ions are in solution / soluble ; keeps cells turgid / prevents drying out / desiccation / wilting ;

                                       (2 marks)

          (ii) temperature; concentration of phosphate ions / eq ; pH ; mass / size / surface area / volume of roots ;   (2 marks)

                                       (Total 11 marks)

3 (*a*) diastole / atrial systole ;
          aortic / pulmonary artery / semilunar valve(s) closed ;
          atrioventricular / mitral / tricuspid valve(s) open ;

                                        (3 marks)

    (*b*)

Part	Function
A	prevents valve inverting ;
B	adjusts tension in A / name / contracts to pull on A ;

                                        (2 marks)

                                      (Total 5 marks)

4 (*a*) bone marrow ;   (1 mark)
    (*b*) granulocyte / granular polymorph / neutrophil / eosinophil ;
          monocyte ;   (2 marks)
    (*c*) platelet / thrombocyte ;   (1 mark)
    (*d*) to enable continued formation of blood cells / eq ;   (1 mark)

                                        (Total 5 marks)

Chapter 3

1

Effect	Auxins	Gibberellins
Promote cell elongation	✓	✓
Promote root formation in cuttings and calluses	✓	✗
Promote fruit ripening	✗	✗
Inhibit lateral bud development	✓	✓ / ✗
Promote the breaking of dormancy in seeds	✗	✓

(Total 5 marks)

2 (a) (i) 3.2×10^5 with cytokinin and 1.37×10^5 without cytokinin ;
$3.2 - 1.37 = 1.83 \times 10^5$; (2 marks)

(ii) not much difference in first three days / converse ;
no increase / division stops after three days without cytokinin /
converse ; cytokinin stimulated cell division ; reference to very
high numbers of cells with cytokinin compared with no
cytokinin / valid use of figures ; (3 marks)

(b) (i) no ; higher concentration gives lower DNA content / converse /
cytokinin has a negative effect on DNA content ; (2 marks)

(ii) in absence of cytokinin DNA replication continues / but
cytokininesis / cell division does not / cytokinin needed for cell
division ; so where no cytokinin doubling of DNA content of
cells occurs ; (2 marks)

(c) presence of auxins needed for cytokinin to work ; reference to
synergistic effect ; high cytokinin : auxin ratio promotes shoot
growth ; low cytokinin : auxin ratio promotes root growth ; (2 marks)

(Total 11 marks)

Chapter 4

1 motor / effector / efferent ; sensory / affector / afferent ; sodium ; pump /
carrier ; resting ; sodium ; potassium; (Total 7 marks)

2 (a) pre-synaptic membrane becomes more permeable to calcium ions ;
inflow of calcium ions ; synaptic vesicles move towards / fuse with
surface membrane of (bouton) ; transmitter substance / named e.g.
released ; exocytosis ; into / diffuses across cleft / synapse ; joins
/binds with receptor on post synaptic membrane ; causes a change in
permeability of post synaptic membrane ; (4 marks)

(b) (i) membrane becomes permeable to Na^+ ions; inflow of Na^+ ions ;
threshold stimulus needed ; correct reference to ion channels ;
(3 marks)
  (ii) (+)28 mV ; (1 mark)
  (iii) 0.6 milliseconds ; (1 mark)
  (iv) diffusion / movement / release of transmitter across cleft /
synapse ; (1 mark)
(c) mimics action of acetylcholine ; attaches to acetylcholine receptors on
postsynaptic membrane ; blocks action of acetylcholine / prevents
action of acetylcholinesterase/ eq ; stimulates postsynaptic cell /
membrane ; (2 marks)
(Total 12 marks)

Chapter 5

1

Statement	Xylem vessels	Phloem sieve tubes	
Possess living contents	✗	✓	;
Provide support	✓	✗	;
Composed of cells fused together end to end	✓	✓	;
Walls contain lignin	✓	✗	;

(Total 4 marks)

2 (a) (i) A: I band / I zone / Isotropic / I region ;
B: H zone / H band / H region ;
C: Z line / Z disc ; (3 marks)
  (ii) myosin ; (1 mark)
(b) becomes shorter / smaller / narrower / disappears / eq ; (1 mark)

(Total 5 marks)

3 hydrostatic ; exo / external ; chitin ; inside / within ; *calcium ; *phosphate ;
*alternatives: magnesium / carbonate / fluoride / strontium

(Total 6 marks)

Chapter 6

1 FSH / follitropin / follicle stimulating hormone ; oestrogen/oestradiol ;
endometrium / uterus lining / womb lining ; secondary oocyte ; corpus
luteum / yellow body ; progesterone ; (Total 6 marks)

2 (a) oxygen / oxyhaemoglobin ; amino acids / named e.g. ; proteins ; glucose
/ blood sugar ; vitamins / named e.g. ; mineral salts / minerals / named /
e.g. ; antibodies ; lipids / fatty acids / glycerol / micelles ; (2 marks)

(b) increases area of contact / surface area between maternal blood and fetal capillaries / eq / reduced diffusion distance qualified ; thus facilitating / making easier exchange of materials between blood of fetus and mother / eq / correct reference to making diffusion between the two easier ;   (2 marks)

(Total 4 marks)

3 (a) (i) percentage falling / fall of 35%; biggest drop in sixties / between 1951 and 1970 ; some evidence of flattening / reference to figures ;   (2 marks)

   (ii) lower percentage of men with low sperm counts at beginning ; numbers increasing during the period / increased by 13% ; both fall 1971 – 1980 ; fall in percentage of men with high sperm counts is greater than rise in percentage of men with low sperm counts / converse ; biggest rise in numbers in sixties / corresponds with drop in numbers of men with low sperm counts / fluctuations in numbers of men with low sperm counts ; after 1980 figures similar ;   (3 marks)

(b) large numbers do not reach oviducts / site of fertilisation ; many sperm die ; reference to conditions / pH in vagina ; enzymes needed for activation of sperm / reference to capacitation ; many sperm may be abnormal / reduced mobility ;   (2 marks)

(c) (i) stimulated by FSH ; stimulates repair of the endometrium / lining of uterus ; inhibits FSH production ; stimulates LH production ; leads to ovulation ;   (3 marks)

   (ii) in maternal blood / blood stream ; when fat stores mobilised / broken down ; correct reference to diffusion ; correct reference to placenta ; uptake into fetal circulation / fetal blood ; into umbilical vein ;   (3 marks)

(Total 13 marks)

4 Insect small amounts of pollen / less pollen / wind more pollen ; insect pollen heavy / wind pollen light ; insect pollen rough / sticky / sculptured / wind pollen smooth ; insect scented petals / wind pollen no scent ; insect nectar / wind / no nectar ;

Insect: position of stigma / sculptured / sticky ; position of anthers in relation to insect entry ; reference to keel / wing petals ; movement of petals when insect lands ; exposes anthers /stigma ;

Wind: no / reduced petals ; anthers hang outside flower ; attachment of anther to filament ; position of stigma ; feathery / large surface area of stigma ; flowers above foliage ; correct reference to lemma / glumes / palea ;

(Total 10 marks)

Index

INDEX